2/71

PSYCHOLOGICAL TECHNIQUES
IN DIAGNOSIS AND EVALUATION

THE AUTHORS

THEODORE C. KAHN, Ph.D.

Diplomate in Clinical Psychology, American Board of
Examiners in Professional Psychology

Chief, Psychological Service, United States Air Force
Hospital, Wiesbaden, Germany

Lecturer in Psychology and Education, University of
Maryland European Division

MARTIN B. GIFFEN, M.D.

Diplomate of the American Board of Psychiatry and
Neurology

Chief, Psychiatric Service, United States Air Force Hospital,
Wiesbaden, Germany

Consultant in Psychiatry, Surgeon, United States Air Forces
in Europe

Psychological Techniques
in
Diagnosis and Evaluation

by

THEODORE C. KAHN, Ph.D.

and

MARTIN B. GIFFEN, M.D.

PERGAMON PRESS

NEW YORK · OXFORD · LONDON · PARIS

1960

PERGAMON PRESS, INC.
122 *East 55th Street, New York 22, N.Y.*
P.O. Box 47715, Los Angeles 47, California

PERGAMON PRESS LTD.
Headington Hill Hall, Oxford
4 & 5 Fitzroy Square, London, W.1

PERGAMON PRESS, S.A.R.L.
*24 Rue des Écoles, Paris V*e

PERGAMON PRESS, G.m.b.H.
Kaiserstrasse 75, Frankfurt-am-Main

Library of Congress Card Number 60–12389

PRINTED IN GREAT BRITAIN BY THE CAMPFIELD PRESS, ST. ALBANS

TO SHIRLEY AND MARGARET

PREFACE AND ACKNOWLEDGEMENTS

ALL medical specialties have a legitimate interest in the function of clinical psychology as an aspect of medicine. In the non-medical professions, lawyers, clergymen, educators, social workers —to name but a few—have occasion to refer to psychological reports or to the literature on psychological testing many times during their careers. This book is intended to give those who have dealings with clinical psychologists, an understanding of what a psychologist is, how he functions, and how he arrives at his conclusions.

Since it has not been our purpose to prepare a textbook for use by professional psychologists, we have not attempted to mention all the various techniques in current use, nor to confine our illustrative materials to tests whose use is universally sanctioned on the basis of scientific validity. Instead, we have employed illustrative models that are: (1) well known and universally popular; (2) methods that we believed to be especially suitable for didactic purposes; and (3) tests in which we have a special competence because we have designed and developed them ourselves.

Credit goes to James R. Gamble, Jr., Captain, USAF (MSC), Psychiatric Social Worker, USAF Hospital, Wiesbaden, Germany, for editing the manuscript, as well as assisting in the task of getting it ready for publication, and to Mrs. Lydia Williamson for typing the entire manuscript. We wish to thank the following physicians for reading the manuscript and offering constructive suggestions: Dr. Harold G. Nichols, Dr. David A. Turner, and Dr. Herbert Kritzer of the Psychiatric Department, and Dr. Donald B. Strominger of the Pediatric Department. We thank Major-General Harold H. Twitchell, Surgeon, United States Air Force in Europe, and Colonel Thomas H. Crouch, Hospital Commander, for their encouragement in this project. We feel that those we have mentioned have had a vital share in any contribution we may have made.

T. C. K.
M. B. G.

Wiesbaden, Germany.

CONTENTS

Contents

FOREWORD

FOR THE past twenty-five years it has been my privilege to counsel and consult physicians about mentally ill patients, as well as to teach medical students and residents in psychiatry. During the years, I have been repeatedly impressed by the degree of ignorance present in medical school graduates in psychiatry and other branches of medicine about psychological testing. Psychological tests offer a source of information about the functioning and influence of the unconscious in individuals with any kind of illness. These test responses can and usually do throw considerable light on the conflicts and anxieties that play a role in illnesses of patients. The understanding of the use of these tests and their limitations is of importance if one is to be able to use this source of laboratory help. In the sense that doctors in many fields fail to understand adequately the way in which x-ray techniques or hematological studies can be of help in the diagnosis of illness, so is there a lack of understanding of the way in which psychological testing can help in the diagnosis and evaluation, not only of psychiatric illnesses, but also in many somatic illnesses in which emotions play an active role.

In their text, Drs. Kahn and Giffen have expressed themselves in simple language, and have covered the area in which psychological techniques may be used.

While one may differ in some particular aspects with the text as presented by the authors, certainly the work as a whole is of such excellent caliber that such differences are not of great moment. The book is easy to read, and can be read rapidly for a first reading. One can then return to the area of particular interest and find sufficient detail in the exposition of that material to answer most questions. This book is a sorely needed and timely discussion of the subject of psychological techniques in various diagnoses and evaluations.

BENJAMIN HARRIS BALSER, M.D.

Director of Psychiatric Research and Training, St. Luke's Hospital. Asst. Clinical Professor of Psychiatry, College of Physicians and Surgeons, Columbia University.

CHAPTER I

CLINICAL PSYCHOLOGY AND MEDICINE

IN THE infancy of medicine it was not difficult to acquire all the available knowledge and techniques necessary to diagnose and prescribe a course of treatment for a patient. Whether the diseased state was explained as a confusion of humors, or infestation of demons, the physician could carry out with clarity an approved and accepted regimen. As individuals freed themselves from superstition and the chains of their period, and critically observed the human in health and disease, a body of factual knowledge concerning abnormal states was developed. With the addition of new techniques in diagnosis, and improved treatment, it became increasingly difficult for any one human being to remain proficient in all phases of medicine. Because of this, specialization became a necessity. With specialization came more knowledge, perfection of techniques and treatment, which required years of study and practice before the individual physician felt qualified. Specialties themselves have divided and subdivided. This, however, is not peculiar to medicine, but is found in all modern sciences. Yet, even with this high degree of specialization, medicine is not a self-contained science, but must and does rely on other specialties and fields for assistance. Clinical psychology is one of these.

The practitioner of medicine, unless he has specialized in the field of psychiatry, usually links psychology with his undergraduate academic studies, and rarely, if at all, concerns himself with this field once he enters in the studies of medicine. He becomes more than twice removed when he engages in the practice of medicine. In one's medical studies, the greatest emphasis has been focused on the organic aspects of the human body, with detail on cellular and tissue structure; their changes in various disease states and aging processes. In many instances, it has been our experience that while the physician is well-versed in the physiology and pathology of the human, he is many times perplexed at the

1

symptomatology which he cannot measure with his diagnostic instruments and procedures. It is impossible for him to conceive of any approach to this conglomeration of cells and tissues, other than organic. Unfortunately, most medical curricula have given too little attention to the emotional and psychological growth and development of the human. As a result, many physicians are ill-equipped to fathom the discomforts and disease states which can, and do, arise from faulty emotional and psychological growth. They have not been given the necessary understanding and knowledge to comprehend the defensive procedures and maneuvers the organism uses to keep an emotional homeostasis. They can perceive, follow, and discuss the pathological physiology, the changes that accompany organic disease states, and with fair accuracy predict further changes and reparative processes in the field of organic medicine. To the physician, psychological and psycho-physiological changes do not appear to be orderly, rational and understandable. In spite of the indivisability of the human organism, we are prone, from our organic training, to regard the patient as a collection of organs, anatomically arranged, with little appreciation of the individual before us; his needs, hopes, fears, and their influence on his pathological state.

In many instances, even the slightest inkling that the symptoms are of a non-organic nature, will either end in the patient being labelled "neurotic" and sent on his way, or rapid referral to a psychiatrist will ensue. Sooner or later, a psychiatric report, which may also include a psychological protocol, will find its way to the referring physician. Upon receiving the consultation report from the psychiatrist, he may accept the report as he would any consultation from another M.D. In reading over the psychological protocols and the findings of the clinical psychologist, he may be perplexed at the information, and, if he is inquisitive, question how one could logically arrive at definitive points about an individual from blocks, pictures, ink spots, and other seemingly childish paraphernalia. Yet, with his professional achievements, his education, training, and specialized techniques, the clinical psychologist can, as any other specialist, render valuable insights into the status of patients. His capabilities run the gamut of assisting in the determination of origin, diagnosis, and prognosis of disease states, as well as aiding in the measurement of the severity of an illness.

He can evaluate the defensive strength of an individual, as well as the weaknesses in the protective armor, and estimate how these can withstand the probing of therapy. He can evaluate the therapeutic procedure, the clinical gains in therapy, and relay this information to the therapist.

The concept of a team of individuals necessary to understand illnesses and sufferings is not a new or unheard of aspect of medicine. In a group or hospital setting, the individual patient, while under the care of one physician, is seen directly or indirectly by many specialists who co-operate in the understanding of the changes occurring. If disease states were always consistent with their prodromal signs, course, and termination, and each disease had uniqueness so that it could, at a moment's observation, be differentiated from all other disease states, the services of specialists would not be needed. This is not the case, and herein lies the fascination of medicine; the knowledge and experiences of a group of individuals is necessary to assist in the diagnosis and treatment of patients. If the physician depended merely on his history and physical examination for a determination of diagnosis, many diseases would probably be recorded inaccurately, or merely as ill-defined states. Certainly, a program of preventive medicine and early detection of disease states and prognostication would be at a primitive level. The use of diagnostic aids and specialized techniques has become an ingrained and indispensable part of the practice of medicine.

In some cases, these special procedures are performed by M.D's. In other instances, individuals who are not M.D's are called upon to assist in the ministration of the patient. The bacteriologist and biochemist perform an important and definitive function and materially assist in the practice of medicine. The clinical psychologist, as these other non-medical men, deserves an honored place in a profession dedicated to the understanding of abnormal states. The clinical psychologist in a clinic or hospital setting is allied most closely with the psychiatric department, but because he is an important member of this group, it should not be construed that his whole function is merely one of assisting in this branch of medicine. Actually, he can function in a much wider range. With our modern concept that the patient cannot be divided into a psyche and soma; that the individual responds as a whole to

insult, whether it be of a physical or emotional nature; the psychologist can render aid to other branches of medicine, offering a
more complete understanding of the total problem confronting
the physician.

To the neurologist and neurosurgeon, the psychological battery
of tests is often an important diagnostic aid in confirming sus-
picions of a new growth within the cranial cavity. At times the
physical findings, specialized x-ray studies, and electro-encephalo-
grams show themselves to be within normal limits, or so equivocal
as to be considered of little significance. Yet in the psychological
tests, patterns may form to give substantial support to a diagnosis
of tumor or degenerative disease. Also, these tests have been
capable of localizing the site of the lesion. On occasion, we have
been called in to evaluate patients who had previously been diagnosed as "hysterical", but when seen psychiatrically, there was a
marked suspicion of organic disease of the brain. Psychological
testing further substantiated this position, and the lesion was
proven at surgery. The neurologist and neurosurgeon do not confine their interest in a psychological examination to aid diagnosis
and localization, but also ask for assistance in estimating the
amount of damage a patient sustained by trauma or surgery. An
accurate estimate of loss due to intellectual impairment is difficult
to make by observation alone. Correct estimates are important for
medical-legal aspects, compensation, and future planning for the
individual. To say that damage is present is as vague as saying
that an individual has a temperature. Without a thermometer to
measure the degree of temperature the seriousness of the disease
may not be noticed. Psychological tests can determine the percentage of loss of intellectual and abstract function with reasonable
accuracy.

On a large and busy pediatric service the clinical psychologist
serves a much needed support function. With the establishment of
well-baby clinics, and their widespread use, problems of delay in
mental growth and development and deviant behavior can be
detected at an early age. With psychological evaluation, even of
the very young, a great deal of information can be obtained.
Seeming backwardness or mental defectiveness as reported by
the family, may on testing prove to be emotional blocking. With
proper handling, and assistance, these children can be led toward

normal development. Since a level of mental ability can be obtained on very young infants, it is advisable in cases of adoption of children to evaluate the infants psychologically before final papers are signed. The pre-adoption examination should never be considered complete until a psychological evaluation, including testing, is done. This should be as much a truism as "no cardiac examination is complete unless an EKG is performed". The authors have personally had occasion to see the grief that may arise in future years without an examination of this type. Quite often in educational settings, the psychologist functions almost alone in assisting the teachers and principals in understanding the emotionally and intellectually restricted child; as well as the exceptionally bright child. He is capable of screening the problems referred, and recommending the more serious ones for treatment. He assists in planning programs for the exceptional child by advising teachers of the personality and educational problems which his tests have disclosed. He can explain the probable origin and the severity of the difficulty so that the teachers can carry out their functions more effectively.

With adults, as with children, it is necessary that we have at our disposal all the available data, including the psychological report, before we can proceed to a logical and firm therapeutic regime. The symptoms of a neurosis and functional psychosis can merely be observed, not outlined or fixated in any area of the body. A biopsy of tissues will not, at least with our present techniques, give a clue as to their origin, malignancy, progression or recession. Therefore, the psychiatrist must rely on the clinical interview. The clinical interview, however, has many drawbacks to early understandings of the origin of precipitating events leading to the specific symptomotology. The patient is, for the most part, a poor observer of events leading to his present mental state. His illness may be of such a nature that it is impossible for him to relate his difficulties. He can actively defend himself by his use of words, giving of answers, or denials, which do not convey his true feelings. He may consciously neglect to convey sufficient information to aid the physician in arriving at a working diagnosis and an understanding of the dynamics which have caused the deviant behavior. Often it takes time and effort before an individual feels free to relate his feelings. It requires much experience in

B

interview techniques before one can use this method to gain an understanding of the dynamics which make up the personality.

The psychological test is structured differently from the clinical interview, and the dynamics of this examination are not quite the same as a face-to-face conversation. The test materials are usually unfamiliar to the patient, and there is no idea of any correctness of answers. The patient can project himself into the test, revealing his personality even though he may be guarded and resistive. He will meet these new stimuli in a manner characteristic of the way he reacts to untried and untested experiences. In some instances, a faster and more complete picture of the individual's personality becomes evident. With the information gleaned from the psychological test, the physician can have available a clearer concept of the dynamics involved. Often this facilitates a more rapid entry into the problem areas of the patient.

Psychological testing should not be conceived of as a mere laboratory procedure in a class with routine tests on blood and urine. It should be viewed as a specialized procedure like the visualization of the interior of the body by radiographic techniques, or the observation on tissues reported by the clinical pathologist. Both of these specialists can shed light on morbid states; their severity, origin, and treatment potentials. The clinical psychologist can use his specialized techniques to visualize a little more clearly and rapidly, the faulty areas of development, and the malignant tendencies in the personality of the patient.

The best appraisal from a psychologist is obtained if a consultation is of a positive nature. It should not be conceived of as a vague hope that something might be found to make the diagnosis. The referring physician should have a definite reason for his referral, and prepare his patient as he would for any other medical or diagnostic procedure. The consultation request should cover the pertinent and significant points in the patient's history and it should mention the specific areas of the psychiatrist's interest. To state merely "request psychometric testing" is insufficient. The psychologist must be given enough information to know which of the many different kinds of tests and techniques are most appropriate for the problem at hand.

In medicine, then, the physician calls upon the clinical psychologist to assist in formulating the diagnosis, uncover the dynamics, assess the severity of the illness, ego strength, and the presence of destructive behavior or suicidal intent. The psychologist's findings help ascertain competency in medical-legal matters and in the evaluation of short or long-term therapeutic results. By using objective measurements he helps determine amount of loss suffered by patients with organic lesions of the brain. He assists in the evaluation of the physically handicapped by probing for aptitudes and disclosing vocational interest patterns. He assists materially in the study of emotionally ill children. His tests and techniques are basic in the evaluation of new therapeutic methods and to all aspects of neuropsychiatric research.

In the chapters that follow we hope the reader will gain an understanding of the specific application, usefulness, and limitations of some of the tools, methods, and techniques of diagnosis and evaluation psychologists use. We hope that an acquaintance with these will enable the reader to make full use of the new and interesting specialty—clinical psychology.

CHAPTER II

PSYCHOLOGISTS AND THEIR TESTS

THE psychologist, who is confronted with the task of evaluating his fellow human being, has at his disposal all the methods that men have used since time immemorial. The history of assessment of human qualities goes back to the dawn of man. Even animals find it necessary to evaluate each other to determine which is strongest. If several mates are available, which one is selected for procreation? The problem of assessment, as a prelude to selection, represents a major, ever-present preoccupation, and history demonstrates that survival—social and biological—often depends on its success.

Originally, the evaluator who aspired to size up the qualities of another man, had only his eyes and ears to serve him. He arrived at conclusions by what he was able to see and hear. Primitive man was primarily concerned with the physical proportions and the loudness of his protagonist's voice. Later, the question of how well the other could handle the tools of war and the hunt became a major factor in the evaluation of his prowess. A man's reputation and what others said about him played a role in judgment. Herein lie the roots of the case history technique used by modern social workers who attempt to understand a person by his past acts and by what others say about him. Together with other techniques, the psychiatrist still relies strongly on his eyes and ears in the evaluation of signs indicating the presence or incipience of mental illness. The inception of psychological tests can be traced back to the first sampling of behavior under crudely controlled conditions as a means of gauging total or future behavior. Among primitive peoples, the initiation ceremony served this purpose. Skins, scalps, and other trophies of the hunt and war were used as signs of bravery and ability. Tribal judgments were based on the number of these a man could collect and display. Later, performance in tournaments served to discover talent and evaluate future performance on the field of battle. All these methods of forming judgments were, in a sense, the fore-runners of modern psychological tests, since a limited sample of behavior was used as an aid in forming a total judgment.

Each method of assessment has its own peculiar advantages and weaknesses. Taken as a whole, the available methods of judging a human being—both primitive and their modern counterparts— are grossly inadequate to the job, and always will be. We can conceive of no magic method that will accurately reflect the infinite complexities of the human personality, its variegated nuances, fathomless depths, or unpredictability in new situations. Most critics of psychological methodology expect too much. Most defenders of this methodology promise too much. The human being with over nine billion unpredictable cortical synapses defies predictable adherence to any known laws. Yet, we must somehow deal with this colossus—the human personality—if we are to have any kind of a science of behavior. We certainly cannot give up before we start. Neither can we admit failure because success is not always complete.

Over and over we hear the accusation that psychological tests are inadequate. These accusations do not only come from the man in the street, who resents "playing with blocks" as an insult to his maturity, but also from professional persons, from psychologists, from professors of psychology, and even from those who earn their living by using and selling tests. Article after article in the professional literature point out how this or that test has failed to live up to expectations. When one hears this criticism over a long enough period of time, one is, at last, tempted to agree—yes, psychological tests are no good. But then comes the question— where do we go from here?

It is indeed true that psychological methods are inadequate in that they fail to tell us all we would like to know about a person. It would be helpful if those who are verbal about the shortcomings of psychological assessment methods, would recommend a substitute for psychological tests. It would be interesting to see how much better their proposed methods would be than the tests in present use. All acceptable psychological tests have been used many times under varying conditions before being published. A large variety of statistical and other scientific methods are employed to establish the worth of these tests, and the results of their failures and successes are available to the reader in mathematical terms. These mathematical terms may be difficult to understand for those not versed in statistics. Nevertheless, they represent a more scientific means of evaluation than a subjective description based on observation alone.

The distrust of some psychologists of psychological testing is, in many ways, unfortunate. Instead of helping to create sound and more effective testing methods by stimulating extensive research, some brush psychological tests aside as not worthy of serious consideration. They use the methods of clinical observation or case history reporting, in lieu of an analysis of psychological tests. They would prefer duplicating the methods of the social worker and the psychiatrist rather than use the tools that are primarily associated with their own profession. In this connection, Professor William A. Hunt, Chairman of the Department of Psychology at Northwestern University, makes the following observation:

"A profession acquires certain duties and practices that are peculiar and indigenous to the body of knowledge possessed by that professional discipline and that belong, through reason of training in that particular body of knowledge, to the unique skill of its practitioners. Clear examples of these are the allocation of diagnostic testing to the clinical psychologist, and pharmacological and surgical therapeutic techniques to the psychiatrist." Later in his review of the role of the clinical psychologist, Hunt states: "Diagnostic testing is the one area where the peculiar and unique competence of the clinical psychologist is accepted by his colleagues on the clinical team. While the psychiatric contribution to diagnostic testing actually has been a sizeable one, the professional pre-emption of the field by psychology is accepted by psychiatry."[30]

It is not surprising in view of the haphazard training and varigated background of clinical psychologists, that many who are overcritical of psychological tests, are found to have inadequate training and practice in the use of such tests. Some with adequate training are temperamentally unsuited for the administration or interpretation of such instruments. In view of the fact that "diagnostic testing is the one area where the peculiar and unique competence of the clinical psychologist is accepted"[30] one wonders why those psychologists who minimize or deny the value of available psychological test methods remain in the field, instead of retraining for other careers. On the other side of the coin, there is no doubt that the uncritical believer in the "crystal ball" quality of psychological tests, is an even greater menace to the profession. Only by setting standards that are sufficiently high to discourage poorly trained individuals, can we hope to continue progress.

TRAINING AND DUTIES OF CLINICAL PSYCHOLOGISTS

In the United States it is commonly agreed that a specialist in clinical psychology should have a doctor's degree. A period of internship is now recommended for all clinical psychologists. Such interns must work under a qualified clinical psychologist, who is certified by the American Board of Examiners in Professional Psychology. A most important contribution to the ethical and competent practice of psychology in recent times, is the establishment of Specialty Examination Boards who examine applicants as to their ability in three fields of choice: clinical psychology, counseling and guidance, and industrial psychology. These examinations are very thorough, and those who survive them are granted a diploma as specialists in their field. Candidates are admitted to the examination only on proof that they have had at least five years of post-doctoral experience in the field for which they are applying. The qualifications for the diploma in any one of the psychological specialties are rigid, and the examinations are exacting.

An excellent summary of the duties and training of a clinical psychologist is given in the appendix of a booklet, *Military Clinical Psychology*, prepared by the Department of the Army and Air Force of the United States. The descriptions outlined pertain to military functions, but with very little change the duties apply equally well to a clinical psychologist in civilian life:

"Clinical Psychologist

General. As a member of the neuropsychiatric team dealing with the problems of personnel having disabilities of a psychological nature, performs one or more of the duties described in the following paragraphs:

DUTIES

(1) Applies psychological principles and techniques as aids to the diagnosis and treatment of individuals; administers and interprets projective and other psychological tests, including those of personality, intelligence, motor co-ordination, achievement, vocational aptitude, and interests.

(2) Carries out remedial therapy in cases of aphasia, speech, hearing, visual, habit, and motor defects; counsels on educational and vocational problems, and on changes in military occupational speciality for military personnel having neuropsychiatric or other psychological disabilities; assists in or carries out psychotherapy under neuropsychiatric supervision.

(3) Performs experimental research as related to the evaluation of current and proposed methods of therapy and diagnosis, the dynamics of normal and abnormal behavior and problems of personality development.

(4) Provides instruction and training in the principles and practices of clinical psychology to appropriate members of the neuropsychiatric staff and others; assists in the program of orienting officers and enlisted men in personal adjustment problems.

(5) Recommends revision of policies to improve use of clinical psychology personnel; serves as liason officer in clinical psychology between other military and civilian agencies."[62]

The psychologist faces another dilemma which has been the basis of some bitter controversy, among psychologists, psychiatrists and social workers. The problem is, how shall he describe what he has found? Are the old Kraepelinean classifications suitable vehicles for what he has learned about the patient? Should he use diagnostic terms, such as Manic Depressive Psychosis, or Obsessive Compulsive Neurosis, or confine himself to descriptions of actual traits and characteristics which his tests elicited? Many psychologists are in favor of the latter course. They advise, "Don't say that the subject's responses are consistent with schizophrenia"—instead, say, "they suggest the presence of a tendency for irrational and autistic thought processes". In effect, what this group recommends is avoidance of inadequate and controversial nomenclature by confining the report to a description of behavioral interpretation. The psychiatrist, or anyone else, who reads the report would have to decide what classification fits the behavior complex elicited by the test battery.

Unfortunately, avoiding the use of psychiatric terminology solves no problems. It merely places an added burden on the psychiatrist, who is left to decide what category or condition the psychologist is hinting about, or how to catalog the psychologist's "descriptive interpretation" to make psychiatric sense. The studious avoidance of psychiatric terms stems from an "I won't play your game" attitude on the part of the psychologist, and perhaps from the understandable disgust, on the part of a scientifically trained mind, for a highly unscientific way of using vague, overlapping and, in part, illogical terms for classifying human behavior. Psychiatric diagnostic terminology is far from perfect, but what other method of classification is available that will avoid the faults of the present system, without creating a host of new disadvantages? The psychologist who avoids using the presently acceptable psychiatric nomenclature is simply avoiding the responsibility of tying together loose impressions into a meaningful and useful whole. Instead of using tabued psychiatric terms, he offers a space occupying description, defining and redefining symptoms, traits, and characteristics that could be more simply and efficiently communicated if he would only say "hysterical personality". The psychologist does not make a diagnosis. But if his diagnostic impression is to make sense, he must not be too fearful or too proud to speak the language of the people with whom he deals. He should not avoid such sentences as, "Psychological test results are consistent with the diagnosis of paranoid schizophrenia". Otherwise he may find that he is talking in riddles to a very busy man who already has to cope with enough riddles. Naturally, when he reports to persons who are not psychiatrically oriented he must use terms and descriptions which can be understood. Psychiatric nomenclature is entirely out of place in the report of a school psychologist to a teacher or school principal. The words and descriptive terms used, as well as the entire tenor of the report, must be geared to be intelligible and meaningful to those for whom the report is intended.

In the following chapters we shall discuss specific psychological tests selected to illustrate some old and new ideas in psychological testing. Before these tests became acceptable tools of the psychologist's trade, they went through a long, time-consuming, and complicated analytical evaluation. No psychologist concerned with his reputation would dare publish an untried psychological technique. There are many books available describing the method by which psychological and educational tests are evaluated before being considered adequate for use. The statistical methods of evaluating psychological tests are far from satisfactory in their present state of development. Again we are faced with the need to be satisfied with what we have available. We must view statistical evidence with skepticism, realizing that a whole host of selective factors may be present in any given test situation. Under these circumstances test users cannot afford to ignore either personal experience with a test, or the results of sound statistical analysis. A brief look at the type of statistical analysis to which psychological tests are subjected may be of interest.

TESTING THE TEST

Psychological tests may come into being in several different ways. One method is for the designer to observe the characteristics of a particular group of people—such as brain damaged. On the basis of the observations, he extracts typical behavior—such as the brain damaged person's lack of capacity to abstract—and designs a series of tasks requiring varying amount of abstractive ability. The next step for the test constructor is to administer his test to a group of patients having brain damage and noting whether his methods and materials are suitable for revealing the lack of capacity to abstract. Further, he must determine whether those who have the greatest amount of organic damage, as verified by the neurologist, have correspondingly greater difficulty than those whose condition is less severe. After correlating these results, he must test an equivalent group of non-brain damaged persons. The latter are called the control group, and the test constructor must insure that identical conditions of testing prevail for both groups. For example, if one group is tested in a hospital ward and another in their homes, the results of the testing may be influenced by this factor. The two groups must also be equated in other important respects. They must have approximately the same socio-economic background, education, intellectual level, age, and marital status. Different degrees of motivation, interest patterns, racial and religious backgrounds, and an endless number of variables can distort the results of the study. If a test has a mechanical component, and the control group by avocation is more mechanically inclined than the experimental group, a source of error may be introduced.

In addition to a careful matching of groups, the investigator must be certain that he is getting typical subjects. He must insure that his "normals" are actually free from past cerebral disease. On the other hand, he must be just as certain that all of his experimental subjects actually have brain damage. Even if he has used every scientific safeguard to avoid errors in selection, and obtained significant results in his statistical comparison of the groups, he is still far from finished. He must record the type of brain damage in his experimental subjects, and decide whether he is justified in making any statements about brain damaged patients in general. Can he be certain that other normal groups will perform the same as the normal group he used for control? After all this, can it be ascertained that other clinical entities will not give similar results? Has he insured that further tests on a similar group will produce similar results? Different results might indicate a lack of inherent stability in the test. In order to resolve these questions, the minimum treatment of any new psychological test includes three things: standardization, validation, and determination of reliability.

STANDARDIZATION

When a specific segment of the population gives a typical performance on a given test, and this behavior can be correctly anticipated, we may say that the test has been standardized. Every new test must be administered to a large number of individuals who form a definite group or category, such as normals, neurotics or delinquents, before we can say that normative data exists for the group. We must constantly bear in mind that standardization for one group does not imply standardization for any other group. One of the first questions when evaluating a new psychological test is, "On whom are the norms?" That is, on whom was the test used or standardized, and what was the typical behavior of this group? A test standardized on eight-year-old children may not be appropriate for use with nine-year-olds. A test standardized on schizophrenic patients with a city background may not be valid for use with schizophrenics who lived in the country.

Standardization of a test also has another meaning. The test itself must be so constructed that it is capable of being given and scored in exactly the same manner with every administration. The administration of the test is then said to be *standardized*, and it can be stated that the test is scored according to *norms*. These norms can only be established experimentally, and represent a group of responses against which any future individual responses can be compared and evaluated. Individual responses have no meaning unless they can be compared and evaluated in the light of known test behavior.

VALIDITY

If a test measures that quality which it has been designed to measure, we say that the test has validity. A technique without some form of validity cannot be considered a test. Validity may be established by various means, but the validity preferred by psychologists is based on statistical evidence. Among the various types of validity that have been used for test construction are:

Face validity. A weak measure of validity consisting of the impression of the person who reads, reviews or takes the test— a mere subjective opinion.

Content validity. This is also an inadequate measure of validity. It is based on "logical assumption" rather than trial. An example would be a mechanical aptitude test employing a series of mechanical puzzles. Content validity stems from the fact that *mechanical* problems are used to determine *mechanical* ability. However, when the test is given to a large number of students, it may measure general intelligence, rather than mechanical ability.

Construct validity. Like content validity, construct validity lacks proof. It represents the effort to validate the theory underlying the test. If a neurologist arranges a series of tasks which require a patient to make abstractions at various levels of difficulty, and justifies his test on the basis that patients with upper neural lesions have difficulty in abstracting, he is claiming construct validity for his device. Unfortunately, there are many tests of this nature that are popular in medical and psychological practice. In order to deserve confidence a test requires more than mere construct validity.

Empirical validity. The tests of validity mentioned before were obtained solely from an inspection of the test instruments. Empirical validity employs outside criteria, against which assumptions can be checked. The relationship between the hypothetical basis of the test, and the outside criteria may be expressed statistically in a variety of ways. It is important that the statistical method chosen to validate a test is appropriate to the task. Each method has its own unique function, and can be correctly applied only when the experimental conditions justify its use. After the statistical data have been tabulated, we must determine the probable error of our statistical evaluation. Levels of confidence represent the percentage of chance operating in statistical results. Thus, when we say that a certain correlation has a five percent level of confidence, we mean that there are five chances out of a hundred that the correlation we have obtained was the result of pure chance. When a t-ratio or chi-square has a one percent level of confidence, we can be reasonably certain that chance played a negligible role in obtaining the results; in this case, only once in a hundred tries could the results we obtained be attributable to chance alone.

RELIABILITY

Sound validity is only one of the requirements in the construction of a good test. Reliability is equally important, and no test should be used until reliability has been established. A test is reliable if it is internally consistent and inherently stable. This is manifested by similar results under similar circumstances, when the test is administered to the same individuals at different times. Obviously, if we give a test on different days, and obtain a wide discrepancy in results, the reliability may be questionable. We must assume that the test subject has not been coached, and that the conditions of testing are precisely identical during the two testing periods. When two dissimilar test scores are obtained from a test administered to the same person after a time lapse, the test interpreter will not know which of the two scores is the accurate measure of the trait which the test was designed to elicit.

The reliability of a test is expressed as a coefficient of correlation. As with validation, there are several methods of establishing the degree of internal consistency of a test.

The Test-Retest Method

This is most appropriate for establishing reliability of projective techniques. This method requires the test subject to retake the test after a time interval. The most obvious disadvantage of this method of establishing reliability is that the statistical results are influenced by changes in the test situation. It is impossible to recreate the exact environment of the previous testing. The person may have changed during the time interval. The person may have learned some of the test know-how, become "test wise" from his experience in taking the test the first time.

Equivalent Form Test

This requires the administration of two tests that have been equated to obtain the same results. Content of the test must be dissimilar in terms of test items used, so that knowledge gained from one form of the test is not transferable to the other. On the other hand, the two forms must elicit the same skills, traits, or aptitudes. Although the equivalent form test reliability circumvents the objections of the Test-Retest Method, it offers new difficulties, in that the test constructor can never really achieve two measures that are inherently identical.

The Split-Half Method

This method of establishing reliability requires that scores on the odd-numbered questions be compared with scores on the even-numbered questions, or the last half is compared with the first half. This is not applicable to projective techniques, but has some advantages when used with educational or proficiency tests of the paper-and-pencil variety. Basically, it has the same disadvantages as the equivalent form test. It assumes an identity of the paired items.

All approved tests are accompanied by a booklet or manual giving a description of the standardization, validity, and reliability. A good manual will describe all the previous studies and researches of the test. It will list the shortcomings, as well as the advantages, of the technique. As far as possible, all statements will be supported by experimental evidence. The scoring method must be explained so that it can be readily understood and followed.

The manual must give explicit instructions to insure that all subjects are given the test in precisely the same manner, and should suggest fruitful areas for future research. In the evaluation of the results, the psychologist is dependent on the test manual for sufficient normative data to make his test findings significant.

CHAPTER III

NORMALS, CHARACTER DISORDERS, AND DIFFERENTIAL DIAGNOSIS

OFTEN the psychologist is faced with the question, "What label fits best?", "What other labels can apply?", and "What labels do not fit at all?" The psychologist's task is further complicated by the fact that his diagnostic impression must be sufficiently directional to exclude or minimize conflicting possibilities. If there are conflicting impressions, it is his job to account for them systematically and logically, and he must define their dimensions and their possible consequences so that the referring agency can take them into proper account. The lack of pathognomonic signs has already caused a number of "half-and-half" categories to come into existence, such as neurosis-with-character-and-behavior-disorder, or schizo-affective-psychosis. The psychologist must not hedge by simply reporting test findings. He must account for what he finds. It is easy to report the presence of a little of everything, and thus evade the problem of diagnosis.

The psychologist must, at all times, be acutely aware of what can be expected of the normal person. In his eagerness to rule out one classification or another, he may forget that there are also normal people. The psychologist who works in psychiatric clinics or hospitals, easily succumbs to a mental set where he excludes normalcy as a possibility. This is because the so-called "base rate", or rate of expectancy, does not include completely normal people in his zone of consideration. Nevertheless, if he fails to be aware of normalcy can he be truly cognizant of abnormality? What, then, can the psychologist expect as signs or evidence of normalcy on the part of the test subject?

NORMALS AND NORMALCY

Normals are people who conform to "normalcy". Normalcy is defined by each individual culture or social milieu. It is easy to be aware of the fact that normalcy among Panamanian jungle people differs from normalcy in New York City. It is more difficult to remember that there can also be a wide spread in the definition of normalcy within the same national boundaries or even within the limits of the same city, such as New York's Park Avenue and its lower East Side. A person who is perfectly well adjusted in the hill country may test as schizoid or characterological when compared to adjacently living valley people. In the consideration of normalcy, therefore, it is of prime importance for the psychological examiner to be a bit of a sociologist and anthropologist. In many universities training psychologists, the emphasis is on the physical sciences, mathematics and statistics, practically excluding the all-important study of social sciences. The authors believe that the understanding of the individual requires that the culture in which he lives be understood. Understanding of the culture can be facilitated by a knowledge of history, and by exploration of other cultures, past and present. The very concept of "normalcy" requires a background in the social sciences.

In general, we consider an individual normal if he is able to function effectively and obtain satisfaction in three main areas: (1) home life, including marriage, sex, children; (2) job or work situation, enabling him to obtain a sense of contribution; (3) community identifications, local, national, and international. The last named ranges from the satisfaction of friendships with neighbors and interest in local town improvements, to an interest in the welfare of the total human race. Normalcy can also be conceptualized negatively. We can say that an individual is normal if he functions in a given society without getting into any trouble; if neither he nor anyone else feels that he should be treated by a psychiatrist, and if he is able to refrain from the use of psychotic defenses and the over-use of neurotic ones. In short, we could call a person normal, if he remains psychiatrically asymptomatic.

By virtue of the negative definition, the psychologist faces a dilemma when testing for normalcy. The normal persons may show all types of neurotic and even psychotic signs. This usually comes as quite a shock to psychologists who never had occasion to thoroughly test a group of persons adjudged to be normal. The authors have experienced such shocks on more than one occasion when a research project called for the examination of normal

c

populations. When viewing the test records of such persons, one almost has the feeling that some of them "have no business being normals" in view of their pathological records. It is easy for the psychologist, under such circumstances to say, "Ah, wait and see—some day they will have their nervous breakdowns." But a follow-up over years may show that the prediction was wrong. The writers have long ago come to the conclusion that "normal is what normal does" and never mind what stirrings are reflected on projective tests, but not evident in behavior. In our present limited state of knowledge we must reluctantly define being normal as acting normal, and let it go at that.

Rorschach Indicators of Normalcy

We must not consider the task of delineating the normal—or normal acting—individual by means of psychological tests as completely hopeless. Almost every psychological instrument attempts to give some indication of normalcy, even if it is only an absence of pronounced pathology. Unfortunately, the tester or test evaluator becomes the arbitrary yardstick of the absence of pathology. If the testee's responses match his own, the patient is "healthy". To avoid such pitfalls, Klopfer and others have

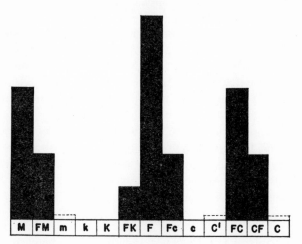

| M | FM | m | k | K | FK | F | Fc | c | C' | FC | CF | C |

FIG. 1. The normal Rorschach psychogram.*

*From *Projective Techniques*, Bell, J. E.[7]

described the expected Rorschach pattern of the normal person in Figure 1, and have justified this pattern with good logical theory, but with little empirical support.

Analyzing the graph, we note that the normal person is pictured as having a goodly amount of creative imagination and capacity for forming inter-personal relationships (M). He is able to express primitive instinctual drives (FM), but these expressions do not outweigh the indices for control (M and F), as is the case among persons who are emotionally immature. Emotional tensions (m) are present, but they are minimal. Signs of basic instability (K) and paralyzing anxiety (k) are absent. There are no responses suggestive of gross sensuality and non-socialized behavior (c). Past emotional trauma leave their traces lightly (C'). As a whole, the normal personality is dominated by perceptual level, contact with reality, stability and basic intelligence (F). There is also a capacity for insight and introspection (FK), as well as tact, and an awareness of the environment (Fc). Finally, the normal person is expected to demonstrate ability for appropriate affective response, without loss of spontaneity, warmth, and artistic creativity (CF). He can be impulsive and explosive (C), although this trend is minimal and held in check by controls which were discussed previously.

The Kahn Test of Symbol Arrangement (*KTSA*)

This test describes the normal person in a somewhat different manner. The two basic approaches to performance on this test consist of emphasis on form and meaning. Three basic types of form orientation are possible:

1. Form concept confined to the objects used on the test only (D).
2. Form of the test objects applied to things in the world outside the test (X).
3. Form consciousness in the sense of emphasis on the color (F) and appearance of the test objects (E). These represent subjective reaction to form.

Also, there are three basic meaning orientations:

1. Meaning with substance (Y).
2. Pure meaning (Z).
3. Autistic meaning (A).

Autistic meaning represents meaning that is unintelligible because it avoids the obligation for social communication. Since the symbolic meaning of the test objects is universal in a given culture, the respondent must make private use of what is essentially public property. Normalcy, therefore, excludes the use of "A" responses, except among young children, where autism represents the development of early psychic ideational processes. Empirical evidence indicates that "Z" responses dominate among intelligent normals. "D" is seldom used. "Y" is present, indicating the presence of reality discernment. "F" or "E" is usually present, with perceptive "E" and artistic "F" trends. As will be mentioned in the chapter on neurosis, too much "Y" is not healthy. Reality discernment must not outweigh idealism and active imagination "Z". On the other hand, stereotyped idealism (also reflected by a "Z" score) represents intellectually accepted but not emotionally experienced symbolic associations. The experienced clinician can tell the difference by internal structuring of the test protocol.

If "normal" means "average"—or behavior that approximates a norm—then "abnormal" includes above average as well as below average. Because of this, the term "normal" has come into disrepute. There is increasing evidence that future testing will concentrate on the abnormal to the right of the line representing the mean, as it has in the past concerned itself almost exclusively to the left of this line. In a highly specialized civilization, such as ours, there is increasing need to identify and attempt to understand the intellectually and ethically superior man.

It may be interesting to observe at the present juncture what psychologists can offer in their attempt to discover the talent of creative leadership. One of the first things that might occur to us is the idea of high I.Q. There is considerable evidence to show that exceptionally brilliant persons do not score exceptionally high on the standard intelligence tests. Some talents are so highly specialized that an I.Q. test is unable to measure them. It has been found that projective tests such as the Rorschach, Mosaic, and Thematic Apperception Tests are more adequate instruments for the identification of genius. (We do not mean "genius" as defined by high scores on I.Q. tests.) Some tentative signs suggestive of exceptional brilliance are as follows:

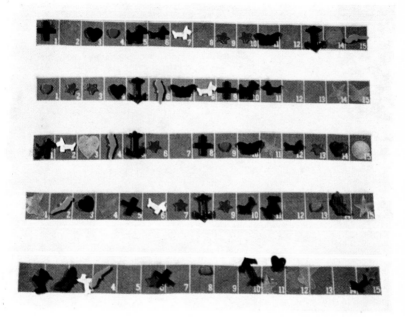

(Approximately $\frac{1}{10}$ size)

PLATE 1

Five different arrangements with the KTSA are shown. Top row represents superior adult's use of similarity and size simultaneously. Second row shows color as basis of arrangement. Below this is a child's attempt to place objects together to tell a story. Fourth row represents balance and design. Last arrangement is typical of psychotics with organic brain disease.

The Rorschach

1. A large percentage of whole card responses when these responses represent effective integration of smaller detail concepts. This is sometimes called "Z" tendency on the Rorschach Test and is not usually reflected in formal scoring.

2. A large percentage of good original responses. Original responses or non-populars, are those which are not seen by the average person.

Either one of the above patterns may be suggestive of unusual ability. In each case, we would expect the presence of some color dominated responses (CF), which indicates sufficient lability and drive stemming from instinctual needs (FM). This creates sufficient tension to motivate the person to seek release through creative activity (M).

The Mosaic and Thematic Apperception Tests

On the Mosaic Test we would expect the use of many colors and the construction of a complete and highly imaginative scene. Much depends on the type of genius we are looking for. The Thematic Tests permit free reign of the imagination and they are capable of eliciting a whole range of imaginative conceptualizations verbally expressed.

The KTSA

On this we would expect greatest emphasis on pure meaning "Z" in the symbolizations. Among physical scientists, "E" (form, construction, and balance) might be prominent. Color "F" would be present among artistic people. The exceptionally gifted individual would have a minimum or absence of "C" responses since his versatility enables him to vary his performance creatively. He probably would not arrange the objects "just as I had them before" (C). He might connect the various objects logically in story form. At least one of the arrangements would be based on similar shapes "E", but usually another concept would be included so that similar shapes would be only one of the factors contributing to the arrangement. "I put all similarly shaped objects together— starting with the largest objects and going to the smallest", or "similar shapes together and alphabetically". Since there are well over a thousand billion different ways in which the objects can be combined on the strip, the subject has considerable opportunity for use of his imagination. (See Plate 1.)

In spite of the theoretical considerations of how the person with superior creative endowment may act on being confronted with psychological tests, there is no real evidence available as yet on this subject. The isolated studies that have been made on creativity manifested on tests, are too few in number and limited in scope to be conclusive. More research is needed in order to fully explore the important study of superior creative ability.

We must not assume that a person with high endowment will necessarily be motivated to use it for the benefit of mankind. A consideration of the manner in which we use our abilities brings us face to face with another area of psychological exploration. At the risk of over-simplification, we may say that the normal person directs his aggressive drives primarily toward the outside world, and in the process diverts them into socially acceptable outlets and activities. The neurotic tends to invert these drives so that they are directed at the self instead of the outside world, and they become self-punishing with hosts of resulting symptomatology. If the neurotic mechanisms are non-somatizing, the expression of the neurotic impulses may be reflected outwardly as projections of the self. Manifestations of these impulses are found in obsessions, over-identification, compulsions, repressions, and emotional blockings.

Character and Behavior Disorders

Among non-psychotics who do not use self as a target there remains only one other avenue for the dissipation of psychic pressure. For these people, society or the representatives of society, becomes the primary target of their drives. Kindled by anxieties, and nurtured by aggression, they spend themselves in seeking retribution for the frustrations which life imposes. Those who use society instead of self as their target, are referred to as having a character and behavior disorder. They are sometimes visualized as lacking a superego or conscience. They are amoral, opportunistic, and sometimes clever. The range of behavioral symptomatology of the character disorders is vast.

Most projective tests offer signs typical of character and behavior disorders. However, the patient's case history is the most effective tool for the identification of these conditions. One danger of relying solely on the interview and the case history is that some of these persons are able to dissimulate their true nature. As a matter of fact, this very act of dissimulating and denying their basic aggression constitutes one of the recognized symptoms of one sociopathic personality type.

The Wechsler

The practical matter of identifying persons with characterological defects by means of psychological tests follows theoretical speculations of reasons for the existence of this category of human being. One explanation, namely that some types of characterological symptoms stem from mental deficiency, is supported by impressive empirical evidence. Some authors find that a characteristic pattern of mental deficiency is associated with delinquent behavior. On the Wechsler Test, the expected psychograph for adolescent delinquents is low on information, comprehension, arithmetic, digit span, and similarity scores. This contrasts with relatively high scores on the performance tasks. Mental defectives without prominent characterological symptoms appear to obtain relatively higher comprehension subscores (compared to the average of all their subscores) than delinquents. Wechsler points out that, "the most outstanding single feature of the sociopath's (delinquent) test profile is his systematic high score of Performance as compared to the Verbal part of the scale".[65] Wechsler also noted that a "good score is frequently made by the sociopath on the Picture Arrangement Test, a finding that is surprising because this test has been interpreted as measuring social intelligence. If this interpretation is correct, a distinction must be made between intellectual understanding and affective acceptance of conventional behavior".[65] Table 1 shows how personality variables may be ascertained from the Wechsler sub-test scores.

The KTSA

Since "affective acceptance of conventional behavior" can be manifested by the acceptance or rejection of socially formed symbols, it is not surprising to discover that tests such as the Kahn Test of Symbol Arrangement elicit typical response patterns from sociopaths. The manual for this test,[33] lists twenty symbols

TABLE 1. PERSONALITY VARIABLE

HIGH SCORES

PERSONALITY VARIABLES	TYPICAL GROUPS	SUB-TESTS
Good Memory, Cultural Interests, Good Education, Verbal Ability.	Obsessive-Compulsives, Ambulatory Schizophrenics.	INFORMATION
Reality Awareness, Capacity for Social Compliance, Good judgment.	Hysterics.	COMPREHENSION
Blandness, Anxiety and Stress Tolerance, Good Memory Span.	Schizoids.	DIGIT SPAN
Alertness and Overalertness, Capacity for Concentration.	Obsessive-Compulsives.	ARITHMETIC
Good Verbal Concept Formation, Paranoid Trend.	Patients using Projection, Paranoid Conditions.	SIMILARITIES
High Intelligence, Compulsive or Intellectualizing Defense Mechanisms.	Organics, Pre-schizophrenics Anxiety Neurotics, Obsessive-Compulsives.	VOCABULARY
Sophistication, Social Intelligence, Ability to Anticipate Consequences of Initial Acts.	Patients with Narcissistic Character Disorders.	PICTURE ARRANGEMENT
Ability to Recognize Essentials, Alertness, Good Visual Acuity.	Normals, Obsessives.	PICTURE COMPLETION
Capacity for Visual-Motor-Spacial Co-ordination.	Schizophrenics, Normals with Engineering Aptitude.	BLOCK DESIGN
Blandness, Freedom from Emotional Turmoil.	Remains Relatively High Among Deteriorated Schizophrenics.	OBJECT ASSEMBLY
Visual-Motor Ability, Mental Efficiency, Capacity for Learning New Material, High Energy Output.	Obsessives, Manics.	DIGIT SYMBOL

LOW SCORES

SUB-TESTS	TYPICAL GROUPS	PERSONALITY VARIABLES
INFORMATION	Hysterics, Involutional Depressives, Chronic Schizophrenics, Deteriorated Organics.	Superficiality of Interests, Repressive Emphasis, Lack of Intellectual Curiosity, Cultural Differences.
COMPREHENSION	Schizophrenics, Depressives, Sociopaths, Obsessive-Compulsives.	Poor Judgment, Impulsiveness, Hostility against Environment.
DIGIT SPAN	Organics, Depressive Psychotics, Hysterical Personality Types.	Lack of Capacity to Concentrate, Anxiety, Flightiness.
ARITHMETIC	Schizophrenics, Organics, Narcissistic Patients.	Defective Mathematical Reasoning, Lack of Capacity to Concentrate, Loss of Alertness and Reality Awareness.
SIMILARITIES	Schizophrenics, Organics, Sociopaths.	Loss of Power of Abstraction, Literalness, Rigidity.
VOCABULARY	Psychotics and Severe Neurotic Depressives, Neurathenics, Normals with Poor Education.	Limited Educational Opportunity, Naivete, Poor Motivation.
PICTURE ARRANGEMENT	Pre-schizophrenics; Paranoid Conditions, Asocial Personality Types.	Paucity of Ideas, Lack of Ability to Plan Ahead, Difficulty in Interpersonal Relationships, Poor Rapport.
PICTURE COMPLETION	Hysterics, Pre-schizophrenics, Paranoids, Organics.	Poor Concentration, Flight of Ideas, Loss of Perceptive Acuity.
BLOCK DESIGN	Organics, Depressives, Neurathenics.	Loss of Capacity in Spacial-Motor Orientation, Loss of Capacity for Visual Integration.
OBJECT ASSEMBLY	Organics, Depressive Psychotics, Acute Schizophrenics.	Visual-Motor Disorganization, Concreteness, Loss of Concept Formation.
DIGIT SYMBOL	Depressive Neurotics, Psychotic Deterioration.	Loss of Capacity for New Learning, Impaired Visual-Motor Capacity.

used almost exclusively by persons having character and behavior disorders. Additionally, this group may slant the objects in placing them on the strip. The final test score falls into a characteristic symbol pattern in which responses, that are not emancipated from form conceptualization, dominate. Thus, "X" responses are more frequent than "Y" or "Z" responses; the latter representing higher forms of abstractions. It is of interest to note that the symbol pattern most frequently produced by persons suffering from character and behavior disorders resembles the one most frequently associated with children eight to twelve years of age. This raises the question as to whether the social development of the sociopaths was arrested at this level of maturity.

The Rorschach

The sociopath shows his lack of motivation by his typically low number of responses. The record is often constricted by an emphasis on form, usually poor form, given with little elaboration. "Maps", "designs", and other evasive responses are frequent. Primitive concepts such as "clouds", "rocks", "scenery", are also encountered. Often there are no human concepts, but if present, animal movement almost always outnumbers human movement. Responses in which color dominates (CF) are more frequent than those in which color is incidental to form (FC). Callous use of color, or color naming may occur. Sociopaths seldom give any well thought-out original responses on the Rorschach. Instead, they may see the common, popular, and banal things. They emphasize very obvious forms, such as the wings on Card V, or the animals on Card VIII. Anatomical responses seen by these persons often take the form of crude sexual preoccupations such as an x-ray of the pelvis, or a "rear end". These may take on a sado-masochistic coloring in cases where there are acting out potentialities. Frequently one or more cards are rejected with verbalizations, suggesting suspiciousness or egocentricity. The use of white areas on the cards to form concepts is sometimes associated with oppositional and negativistic feelings on the part of the testee.

The TAT

Just as the sociopath performs the "easy way", expending a minimum of effort on the Rorschach, he describes effortless accomplishments on the part of the figures he sees in the Thematic Apperception Tests. On these tests, he indicates his conviction that this is a "dog-eat-dog" world, and that ruthlessness and strength lead to success. There is no place for ethics in the world, and people suffer solely because they fail to use their wits in destroying the evidence of their antisocial acts. High ambitions may be ascribed to the central figure. These ambitions will not be achieved by hard work, but by "getting the breaks", or "knowing the right people". Sociopaths show little emotion or concern with the fate of persons depicted as grief-stricken or forlorn. Instead, emphasis is always on *how* these people got into trouble, and *what* means they find to extricate themselves. Authority figures are typically seen as cynically selfish, and women as weak or despicable. However, much depends on the type of characterological difficulty with which we are dealing. Sociopaths with prominent passive or dependent orientations will offer concepts that are quite different from those with aggressive acting-out potential. These, in turn, will differ from the concepts of persons who cover their antisocial feelings by a screen of over-conformity to social norms. In the latter case, the heroes depicted on the TAT are often true Sir Galahads, who are too noble and free from fault to be realistically human.

The Minnesota Multiphasic Personality Inventory

The MMPI has been used effectively to screen this type of population. As with all paper and pencil questionnaires, the possibility exists that the test subject may slant his responses in a way that will make the best impression on the examiner. On the MMPI there are certain built-in safeguards to warn the interpreter that the individual may have failed to represent his genuine feelings, and that his responses lack validity. Nevertheless, there is the question of how effectively these safeguards operate. When the test signs indicate that the subject has faked, we are left with little to guide us in regard to the direction and nature of the malingering. In spite of these objections a high Pd (psychopathic deviate) score on the MMPI, and projective test indicators of antisocial personality are frequently found together in clinical experience. According to the authors, the Pd scale on the MMPI, "measures the similarity of the subject to a group of persons whose main difficulty lies in their absence of deep emotional responses, their inability to profit from experience, and their disregard of social mores".[29] This description fits the picture of the sociopaths as delineated by other test methods. Social development was defective because of a specific type of intellectual lag or because of faulty symbol formation involving cultural norms.

DIFFERENTIAL DIAGNOSIS

The questions which psychologists are required to help answer usually consist of locating one of several possible causes for the patient's symptoms or behavioral characteristics. For example, psychiatrists who refer cases for psychological evaluation may be looking for evidence to help decide whether their patient is primarily a characterological problem, or a neurotic one. Or the question asked is whether a patient's excitement is part of a schizophrenic process or a manic depressive psychosis. Other common questions are: Can the symptoms be explained on the basis of neurosis, or is there an incipient psychosis present, which may become more virulent with time? Is the patient's behavior ascribable to schizophrenia alone, or are there some organic concomitants? Similarly, the teacher referring a child to the school psychologist usually poses: Is the boy's troublesome behavior in the classroom ascribable to emotional immaturity, to lack of sufficient intelligence to keep up with the class work, or to serious family problems in the child's home? Two considerations are important in the problem of differential diagnosis. These are: (1) predominance of evidence; (2) consistency of evidence.

Predominance of evidence exists when test signs associated with one condition are stronger or more numerous than those of other conditions. This, however, does not always apply because even one weak sign of schizophrenia in an incipient or borderline state may be significant. In general, it is true that the more serious the condition, the less obvious the signs need be to alert us to the presence of the condition. On the other hand, in clinical practice, it is often necessary to tentatively disregard weak signs indicating psychosis or other serious conditions when these are unsupported by confirming evidence. This is particularly true of the test signs which overlap several diagnostic areas. By predominance of evidence, then, we mean quantitative and qualitative dominance as ascertained by the well-trained and experienced psychologist.

Because there is always a qualitative factor involved in the evaluation of a human being, psychologists cannot dispense with simple judgment. The trouble with the strictly quantitative "cookbook" approach to human evaluation is that we are dealing with the cooks themselves, rather than with the ingredients of their stews and puddings. No mechanical guide exists which can tell the psychologist what resources he must draw on to extract a sound clinical impression. Variation of method occurs from patient to patient, and depends on the individual circumstances. When the total resources available to the psychologist are used, overlapping signs are not as perplexing as they may appear at first. For example, patients with brain damage and certain types of schizophrenia may offer similar concrete behavior in their solution to the Weigl-Goldstein-Scheerer Color Form sorting task. Although test performance of these two groups is at times indistinguishable, a differential impression is gained by the fact that this concreteness may be evident among organics who show relatively few other clinical signs and little general deterioration behaviorally. Schizophrenics who exhibit this same degree of concreteness on the test, are obviously ill clinically and show considerable behavioral deterioration. In order to form his impression, in cases such as this, the psychologist must be aware of the patient's case history and his observed behavior.

Consistency of evidence presents somewhat less of a problem. Let us assume that six tests are administered in a psychological battery, and in all but one of these, responses indicate signs of character disorder. No signs are found indicating pathology of a more serious nature. Signs of other conditions, such as neurosis, are scattered and weak. The psychologist can then report that the testing elicited responses suggestive of a characterological condition, and that the test battery was consistent—with the exception of one test—in reflecting the expected indicators of this condition. He must account for the presence of the inconclusive signs and offer an explanation for the fact that one of the tests failed to register any signs of character disorder. Perhaps the psychologist noted that the patient was getting tired when this test was given. Perhaps rapport had not yet been established.

In spite of the fact that consistency of trends is an important requirement for the formulation of clinical impressions, relatively little research has been done in this area. Most psychological test research concerns itself solely with one test at a time. Tests are then criticized if they fail to measure up to statistical expectations. However, even trends that are not statistically significant in themselves, or are representative of only one technique, may be valuable in diagnosis when taken cumulatively.

The test battery must be chosen with care and the materials used for testing must represent a sufficient variety to enable an assessment of different approaches to the study of the patient's personality. It is urged that the battery include objects that the patient can freely manipulate, for example, the mosaic materials, paper and pencil tests, and visually oriented tests printed on cards such as the Rorschach, TAT, and Blacky Pictures. Variety of materials is important since persons react differently to different kinds of material. Physiological and psychological factors determine whether verbal, visual, or manipulative tests are most suitable for eliciting information. When the test situation is limited to one medium, opportunities for obtaining accurate results may have been overlooked.

The evaluator should not hesitate to admit that signs are inconclusive and conflicting. Psychologists realize that sometimes they can only confirm the psychiatrist's dilemma in regard to a difficult diagnostic decision. However, even this has its value, for it will establish the presence of the conflicting and puzzling aspects in the case and will suggest that the psychiatrist has not overlooked anything which could have contributed to a diagnostic solution. It rarely occurs that the psychologist is unable to throw some light on the problem. Even if a patient fails to respond to the majority of the test stimuli which the psychologist offers, the very lack of response constitutes a valuable diagnostic aid. This is especially true if the testee fails to react to some stimuli, but not to others.

Finally, in the evaluation of the kind of stimuli to which the patient responds, great care must be taken in coming to conclusions. On the Rorschach, the assumption that the patient will respond in a stereotyped manner to such stimuli as Card IV and VII (so-called Father and Mother image cards) is one of the many concepts in projective psychology that deserves to be regarded with skepticism. If we consider only what is referred to as "card pull", the power of the materials to stimulate characteristic responses, we would not have sufficient grounds for explaining the fact that many patients express their feelings toward parental or authority figures on Cards IV and VII. Neither the hugeness, blackness, and strength implied in Card IV, nor the vague femininity reflected on Card VII, would be enough to elicit the corresponding responses were it not for "test-subject push" which is independent of the "card-pull". The testee has a need to give expression and release to disturbing emotional drives. The "patient push" reinforced by "card-pull" (or its equivalent in other tests than the Rorschach) combine forces to give the test responses. It is the pressure of his psychic drives, "patient push", seeking any possible outlet, that causes the testee to grasp the proverbial straw in order to give expression to his fears, anxieties, and resentments. His needs are like those of a stream pursuing a course down a mountain without a suitable path in which to run. The stream flows even in the absence of a good river bed. So it is with the testee's stream of thoughts. His need to express himself causes him to offer dynamically meaningful responses even when the pull of the materials used is relatively weak. However, this in no way implies that the choice of stimuli materials is not important. Even the pull of gravity cannot overcome some obstacles and downhill streams may become dammed. A careful selection of test materials is essential to insure the smooth and unhampered flow of dynamically significant material.

CHAPTER IV

INTELLIGENCE

WHAT is intelligence? Some psychologists have defined it as the capacity to adjust to, or change environment; the power of meeting any situation, especially a novel one, and resolving any difficulties encountered. Or is it better to say intelligence is that which is measured by intelligence tests? We know people who are pathologically impractical or even psychotically so, whose intellectual level as measured by tests is far above average. How can we say then that intelligence represents the capacity to adjust to the environment? Perhaps we should define it as the ability to solve problems. Yet we know that there are highly intelligent people who block or freeze when confronted with certain types of problems. They may even fail simple arithmetic or information questions during various mental states. Perhaps it would help to think of two types of intelligence; the type that an intelligence test measures, and the kind that a person is able to utilize in life situations. The first we might call "theoretical" intelligence, since it is determined by the theoretical implications built into the intelligence test. The second we could consider the "practical" intelligence, which is the amount of intelligence a person is actually able to utilize in everyday situations, such as his job, interpersonal relationships, and marital adjustment. Unfortunately, the practical intelligence available to an individual is severely limited by an all-pervading, contaminating influence—the person's emotional maturity and health. Practical intelligence is rarely a pure product. This creates a problem for those who attempt to measure the practical intelligence. The theoretical intelligence—a person's capacity to adjust to a specific test situation—is also a rather unwieldy and somewhat unrealistic concept, since it exists in a vacuum isolated from life by the walls of the psychologist's office, and the artificial nature of the test. It is well to remember that the psychologist's measure of a man's intelligence, and the kind of intelligence the person actually uses, are different in many respects.

What then is intelligence? There is no simple answer to this question. If we delve a bit into what factors are responsible for the level of performance that any person attains on an intelligence test, we find ourselves again in a morass of doubt and uncertainty. We face the question of how much "test measured intelligence" is the product of an intellectually stimulating environment (or lack of it) and how much is a native, inborn, congenitally determined combination of skills and mental traits? Research points to the conclusion that the environment can inhibit the development of native ability or stimulate it, but the upper boundaries of intellectual achievement are predetermined by inherited factors. These limitations are particularly evident in cases where a child is born with, or develops any form of brain damage which interferes with intellectual functioning. If the deficiencies result from genetic defects traceable to the inheriting mechanisms of the individual, intellectual capacity may be fixed at a very low level, and further growth may be virtually impossible. On the other hand a child with considerable native brilliance, who is severely disturbed because of emotional reasons, or has limited contact with cultural resources, may find it difficult to raise his intellectual level, until the emotional climate is improved or the cultural deprivation is eliminated.

A perusal of several different types of intelligence tests leads to another question. If "intelligence" is defined as that combination of qualities which an intelligence test measures, how can we allow for tests that differ in content matter, and in the technical level of scoring? It is possible for an individual to be superior on one intelligence test, average on another, and definitely below average on a third. He may have scored high on a test that was heavily weighted with verbal tasks and poorly on one in which manipulation and psychomotor skills were emphasized. Some tests give separate verbal and performance scores, but others in frequent use do not make any such distinction. It is, therefore, always important that those who use the results of intelligence testing know the nature and content of the test involved. We should know on what type of population the intelligence test was standardized, as well as the validity and reliability of the test. In spite

D

of their shortcomings, intelligence tests are the best and practically the only tool available for measuring human capacity.

TYPES OF TESTS

Intelligence tests may be grouped into two large categories; the paper-and-pencil group, and the individually administered tests. Of the two, the individually administered tests are usually far more satisfactory, since each test subject can be observed while performing the tasks. This is important, as motivation, anxiety, or hostility toward the testing situation can materially affect test results. Furthermore, individually administered intelligence tests are usually constructed so that the test subject is able to perform with different types of media. Many react more favorably to a three-dimensional plane than to one of two dimensions.

The paper-and-pencil tests have the greater advantage of permitting group administration, which makes it possible to test many persons at the same time, and certainly simplifies the problem of validation and standardization. However, paper-and-pencil intelligence tests offer neither as accurate, nor as broad, a picture of an individual's mental capacity. Paper-and-pencil tests may be satisfactory for general screening purposes where large groups must be tested. Where there is doubt in an individual case, the individual test becomes a mandatory procedure.

MEASURING INTELLIGENCE

Intelligence is an attribute with many facets, and it is questionable whether an individual's intelligence can be described in a few words or expressed as a simple numerical score. In 1904, Alfred Binet appointed a National Educator's Committee to investigate mental retardation of students in French schools. In collaboration with Theophile Simon, he published the first intelligence test, consisting of thirty items arranged in order of increasing difficulty. With this scale, Binet introduced the concept of Mental Age. A child was assigned a mental age in accordance with the number of tests he passed. In 1912, the German psychologist, Wilhelm Stern, suggested that a test subject's relative inferiority or superiority could be calculated by dividing his mental age by his actual or chronological age. This was called the Intelligence Quotient and is known in abbreviated form as I.Q. The formula developed by the American psychologist Lewis Terman is:[60]

$$\frac{M.A. \ (Mental \ Age) \times 100}{C.A. \ (Chronological \ Age)} = I.Q. \ (Intelligence \ Quotient)$$

Using this formula, if a child has a chronological age of eight years, and the intelligence test indicates a mental age of eight years, the M.A. and C.A. will cancel out, leaving an I.Q. of 100. That is why an I.Q. of 100 is considered "average", because in all such cases the person's mental age is consistent with his chronological age. Some shun the idea of Mental Age, considering it an outmoded concept. The writers do not agree with this point of view. The concept of Mental Age is useful to ascertain levels of mental functioning. Table 2 shows approximate mental ages associated with I.Q. among adults.

TABLE 2. I.Q. AND APPROXIMATE CORRESPONDING MENTAL AGE
AMONG ADULTS*

I.Q.	M.A.
56	8 years
63	9 years
70	10 years
77	11 years
84	12 years
91	13 years
98	14 years

*Adapted from *Measuring Intelligence* by
Terman, L. M. & Merrill, M. A.[60]

In interpreting an I.Q. it should be borne in mind that psychologists allow for an error of ten points—five above and five below the tested I.Q.—as representing the limitations of the test or the testing situation. Certain emotional states may unduly influence the test results. The psychologist must determine whether the test is a true measure of the subject's capacities, or whether it was influenced by emotional factors.

SPECIFIC TESTS IN COMMON USE

The Wechsler-Bellevue Intelligence Scale (Adults)[63]

This test was introduced in 1939 by David Wechsler, Chief Psychologist at the Bellevue Psychiatric Hospital in New York City. In its various forms it has had wide popularity with psychologists all over the world, since it is a relatively pleasant test to take and offers considerable variety of method and media in gauging intelligence. Because of variations in the sub-scores, it can be helpful in arriving at diagnostic impressions. Clinical entities appear to have distinguishing and identifiable sub-test patterns (Table 1).

The various abilities measured by the Wechsler are:

1. Verbal Scale

    A. *Information*: A variety of questions ranging from easy to difficult such as: "How many weeks are there in a year?" "What is ethnology?"

    B. *Comprehension*: A test of logical thinking in which the test subject explains why things are done or why they occur. Examples: "Why should we stay away from bad company?" "Why are laws necessary?"

    C. *Arithmetic*: Simple to difficult arithmetic questions.

    D. *Similarities*: This task requires identification of likenesses between different objects such as: "dog" and "lion", "poem" and "statue".

    E. *Digit Span*: This consists of immediate recall of digits. In the first part, the digits are repeated as they are given. In the second part, the digits are repeated backwards; when the examiner says, "3, 1, 5", the test-subject repeats, "5, 1, 3".

    F. *Vocabulary*: The patient is required to define words ranging from common ones to those rarely used.

2. Performance Scale

    A. *Digit Symbol*: The testee is shown some symbols associated with numerals. Within a given time limit, he must copy the symbols in blank spaces provided on the test sheet, using the numerals as a guide for his work.

B. *Picture Completion*: Part of a picture has been omitted, such as half of a mustache on the face of a man. The subject indicates what is missing.

C. *Block Design*: Using colored blocks, the individual makes designs shown by the examiner. There is a time limit to the performance, and extra credit is given for speedy work.

D. *Picture Arrangement*: A series of pictures are arranged to make the most logical sequence. Time credit is given.

E. *Object Assembly*: The test-subject is given a number of flat cardboard pieces which he must fit together correctly to make a common object, such as a face or a hand. There are time limits for the performance and credit is given for speed.

After an individual completes the above tasks, a verbal I.Q. and a performance I.Q. are derived by looking up the I.Q. equivalents of the weighted scores in a table found in the book of instructions.[63] It is interesting to note that allowance is made for the so-called "mental deterioration" with increased age. In checking the tables, we find that an eighteen-year-old person, having a weighted score of 115 on the Full Scale will obtain an I.Q. of 105; whereas a person between the ages of fifty-five and sixty-four need only a score of 101 to obtain the same I.Q.

Form I of the Wechsler-Bellevue Intelligence Scale was superseded by the revised Wechsler Adult Intelligence Scale (WAIS) in 1958. The revision entailed the complete restandardization of Form I and, according to the publishers of the test, provided a more efficient measure of the intelligence of adolescents and adults from ages sixteen to over seventy-five.[65]

The Wechsler Intelligence Scale for Children (WISC)[64]

The WISC is standardized for children aged five through fifteen. Ten tests yield an I.Q. which is based on weighted scores for each age level, rather than on Mental Age. Five of the tests are verbal and five are performance. A separate I.Q. can be obtained from either the verbal or the performance scale. In spite of the fact that the manual and test materials are practical and easy to use, there are a number of serious objections to this test. Among these are, "evidence that the test may be too difficult at the lower age brackets; Mental Age is difficult to ascertain from the test scores, and scoring of certain verbal items include considerable subjectivity". [18]

Modifications of the Wechsler Scale

1. *Modification for British use*: A number of years ago, the British Psychological Society set up local working parties to inquire into the use of the Wechsler tests in the United Kingdom. As a result, a number of modifications were suggested for both the WISC and the WAIS. To date, British versions of the manuals have not been produced, but a list of modifications is available.* Changes incorporated in the British modification deal largely with English denominations of money and geographical locations familiar to English people.

2. *Modification for use in German-speaking countries*: The German edition of the Adult Wechsler, the Hamburg-Wechsler Intelligence Test Für Erwachsene (HAWIE),† follows the original model in practically every respect except for minor changes in the information and vocabulary. The HAWIK, or Hamburg-Wechsler Intelligenztest Für Kinder,‡ also follows rather closely its USA counterpart. Changes that occur were made because of cultural differences between countries. The surprising thing is not the changes which were made between the German and the USA version, but that the German one is so similar, in spite of the different cultural and educational factors that exist at opposite sides of the Atlantic. Perhaps European culture as manifested by the absorption of skills used for intelligence testing is not as different from USA culture as some people have supposed. Perhaps intelligence test techniques have a much broader interculture applicability than we had dared to hope.

Revised Stanford-Binet Intelligence Scale [60]

At present this is still one of the most popular psychological methods for assessment of the intelligence of children. The writers

* The British Psychological Society, Tavistock House South, Tavistock Square, London, W.C.1, England.

† Distributed by Psychologisches Institut Der Universität Hamburg, Germany.

‡ Distributed by Psychologisches Institut Der Universität Hamburg, Germany.

do not feel—as some psychologists—that the Wechsler Intelligence Scale for Children will make this old, but highly valid, method of ascertaining intelligence levels obsolete. For one thing, a tremendous amount of research has gone into the scale, and its prediction coefficients. The revision of the scale dates back to 1937. The test is applicable to ages ranging from two years to superior adult. Two forms are available—Forms L and M. These are essentially equivalent. In Form L, there is more emphasis on verbal activities; in Form M, the emphasis is on performance. The test materials come in a wooden box and consist of pictures and objects which the child must identify; several diagrams which must be reproduced—some by memory, others by copying. Blocks, a formboard, picture comparisons, beads, string, sticks of various sizes, objects to be counted, mazes, and incomplete sentences are among the items used by the examiner in the test. Early in 1960 a new revision of the test was published which combines Forms L and M and attempts to bring all the items up to date.

Most tasks represent a span in mental age of one to two months. A table at the end of the Binet Manual of Instruction helps the examiner in converting mental and chronological ages into I.Q. levels.

1. Examples of tasks on the Stanford-Binet Test:

   A. Age two years and three months: Show the paper doll and say, "Show me the dolly's hair." Same for mouth, ear, and hands.

   B. Three years and five months: Give the child a pencil, pointing to the circle in the booklet, say, "Make one just like this."

   C. Four years and three months: Point to incomplete drawing in the record booklet and say, "What is this?" Whether the child recognizes it or not, say, "It's a man, isn't it? See he has only one leg. You finish him. Make all the rest of him."

   D. Five years and ten months: Repeat without error: "Jane wants to build a big castle in her playhouse."

   E. Seven years and six months: Child copies a diamond.

   F. Ten years: Child correctly defines eleven words given him by examiner.

G. Twelve years, six months: Child repeats five digits reversed.

H. Thirteen years and ten months: Places disarranged words in proper sequence: FOR THE STARTED AN WE COUNTRY EARLY AT HOUR.

Cattell Infant Intelligence Scale[16] (Ages three months to thirty months)

This method of obtaining mental ages and I.Q.s was developed by Psyche Cattell and its purpose is to make available a downward extension of the revised Stanford–Binet Examination. An illustration of scoring for the third month of life follows:

Third Month

1. Ring, follows in circle (supine).
2. Feeding, anticipates (bottle).
3. Cube, regards (sitting).
4. Spoon, regards (sitting).
5. Fingers, inspects (supine).
6. Chest, lifts by arms (prone).
7. Head erect and steady.

Arthur Point Scale of Performance Tests[4] (Ages five to fifteen years)

Form I of this test has been in use since 1925. A revised Form II is now available and like its predecessor attempts to establish mental levels based on manipulative rather than verbal skills. It offers a means of measuring the abilities of deaf children, those suffering from reading disabilities, those with delayed or defective speech, and those who do not speak a language similar to that of the examiner. Form II has five parts:[5]

1. A test requiring the manipulation of cubes.
2. A form-board requiring the test-subject to place cut-outs in the correct openings.
3. Arthur stencil design test in which the test subject is required to reproduce designs from a combination of cards and cut-out stencils in several colors.
4. Porteus Maze Test.
5. Healy Picture Completion Test.

*Kahn Intelligence Test** (Ages one month to superior adult)

This test is referred to as the KIT, and at this writing is just emerging from its experimental stage. The materials used in this test are the same as those in the Kahn Test for differential diagnosis and personality study. The test was designed to be almost completely independent of cultural and educational environmental factors. In the main, it is non-verbal, requiring performance at various levels of difficulty. In addition to the tasks giving mental ages and I.Q., this new method offers special tests of concept formation, recall intelligence, and motor co-ordination. The evaluation of intelligence of the test subject can be determined, even if he is unable to communicate verbally. Testing the blind (ages two years to superior adult level) can also be accomplished.

1. Examples of some of the tasks on the KIT:
   A. Two to three years: Examiner: "I'm going to hide this doggie and then see if you can find it." In full view of child the examiner rolls the white dog in the strip, places strip in box, puts the anchor, cross, and parrot on top of box saying: "Now find the doggie—show me where I hid it."
   B. Six years: The examiner hands the child the large transparent heart and the small red one, saying,: "Name three ways in which these two hearts are different." PERFORMANCE REQUIRED: Child states size, color, and thickness. SCORE: plus score is given if three qualities are mentioned. Transparancy is acceptable as one of the differentiating qualities.
   C. Eleven years: Examiner places objects on the strip in this order: star, white dog, red heart, cross, star; exposes them for five seconds, mixes them up and asks child to replace them exactly as they were.
2. Examples of the use of the KIT with blind children.
   A. Three to four years: Examiner gives child the two stars and the heart, saying: "Find the one that is different and give it to me. Keep the two that are the same."
   B. Ten to eleven years: Examiner hands child the following objects, two at a time, asking child each time which one

* This test is in the experimental stage.

is the heaviest; the large dog and the large heart; the butterfly and the small dog.

3. Examples of the use of KIT when test subject and examiner cannot communicate verbally.

  A. Two to three years: The examiner takes the red star and the black dog and hands child the other dog and star. The examiner places his red star on the dog, removes and repeats this several times, and finally leaves red star on dog, pointing at the same time to the object child has in his hands and then back to his own objects. Plus is scored if the child imitates the examiner's model by placing the star on the dog as the examiner did.

  B. Eight to nine years: Examiner places two stars, the three dogs, and the red heart on the strip in the sequence shown in the test manual. He leaves the objects on the strip, pointing to them in order to indicate that the child should look at them. After exposing the objects for five seconds he removes them, hands them to child, indicating by pointing to the child and then to the strip that the child is to replace the objects as they were.

Full Range Picture Vocabulary Test[2] *and the Columbia Mental Maturity Scale*[15]

Both of these methods require no verbal and minimum motor responses. Therefore they are especially suitable for cerebral palsy patients and others with impaired physical or verbal functioning. The Full Range Picture Vocabulary Test is available in two forms, each consisting of sixteen cards. Four cartoon-like drawings appear on each card. The examiner has an answer sheet on which are printed certain words to be used with each card. The testee is asked which one of the four drawings best represents the particular word and can respond by pointing. Thus, the test can be given to anyone who can hear or read words and is able to signal "yes" or "no" in any interpretable way.

Leiter International Performance Scale[37] (Ages two to eighteen years)

Leiter believes that this test offers a chance to cope with new situations and represents a better index of brightness than learned or memorized knowledge. His test can be given without language or pantomime. It can be adapted for use with the multiple handicapped. Although this test has many advantages, it is bulky and the cost of the test is relatively high.

Estimating Intelligence from the Rorschach Test

The Rorschach Test has also been used to measure intelligence. Some types of intelligence are more satisfactorily reflected by use of stimuli materials such as the Rorschach offers. This is particularly true of what one might term "creative intelligence", which is by-passed by the average intelligence test. The capacity to organize stimuli, to use the imagination, and to express creative energies, represents the big void in present-day intelligence testing.

Table 3 gives an estimate of the intelligence derived from Rorschach protocols.

TABLE 3. INTELLIGENCE DERIVED FROM THE RORSCHACH*

Level of intelligence	Number whole card responses	Number human movement responses	Number pure color responses	Percent good form responses	Percent animal responses	Percent original responses
Very Superior	10+	5+	4–7	90–100	10–20	30–50
Superior	7–10	5	1·5–3·5	80–100	20–35	0–20
Average to High	4–7	2–4	1·5–2·5	70–80	30–55	0–20
Low Average	3–4	0–2	1·5–0·6	60–70	50–70	0–20†
Morons	1–3	0	4·7	45–60	60–80	30–40†
Imbecile	0–2	0	5·5–8·5	0–45	80–100	40–70†

*Adapted from The Rorschach Test as applied to a feeble-minded group by Beck, S. J.[6]

†Original responses with poor form.

A study of Table 3 shows that in some respects the extremes of intelligence seem to meet. Both very superior people and imbeciles have a relatively large number of pure color (color without form) responses, and likewise a high percentage of original (non-popular) responses. The difference can be found by inspecting the percentage of good form responses. The original concepts of imbeciles almost always have poor form, whereas those of the superior group are of good form. Furthermore, the number of pure color responses found among superior Rorschach records represent only a small percentage of the total number of responses; whereas among imbeciles they may represent over half of the total responses. The striking difference between low and high intelligence records is seen in the number of human movement responses. The capacity to see human movement seems to be related, not only to good emotional health (except in the case of certain types of paranoids), but also to effective use of creative imagination.

In the signs of mental deficiency given below, we note that one of the ten characteristics cited is an absence of human movement. The signs delineated by Klopfer[35] are:

1. Poor form of the concepts perceived.
2. Defining the blot areas instead of saying what they look like.
3. Many pure color responses. Responses where form is not a factor in the perception.
4. No human movement responses.
5. Frequent occurrence of poor whole card responses given on the basis of some details on the cards.
6. Few good whole card responses.
7. Lack of systematic approach in conceptualization. That is, not proceeding from small to large or from large to small details on the cards.
8. Little content variety.
9. High animal percentage.
10. Emphasis on unusual detail.

Group Intelligence Tests

*The Fourth Mental Measurement Yearbook** lists over sixty group intelligence tests, and in addition, almost four hundred tests of special abilities or skills such as arithmetic, science, sensory motor, and clerical aptitudes. It is not within the scope of this volume to discuss these techniques, except to state that group intelligence tests have a very useful place in the general screening

* Published periodically by Gryphon Press, Highland Park, New Jersey.

battery in schools, industry, and the military service. Essentially, their aim is identical to that of the individually administered intelligence test. The great advantage is that these tests can be given to many people at one time. The number is limited only by the amount of room to seat the subjects, and proctors to supervise them. The disadvantages are numerous. By the lack of opportunity to observe individual performance, the psychologist is unable to identify such factors as motivation, test anxiety, and the individual's manner of approach to problem solving. Group intelligence tests are usually speed tests—there is a time limit for each question, and the more answered correctly within a given time limit, the higher the score. There are many individuals who do not perform at their best under such time-stress conditions. Such persons may do significantly better in an atmosphere of greater relaxation, where there is a chance to establish rapport with the examiner. Some test subjects require reassurance during the testing process, and will perform poorly if they do not obtain this needed encouragement. Finally, the observational notes made by the examiner during the administration of individually given intelligence tests, often yield a valuable clue to the understanding of the personality of the test subject. Behavior during the test will enable the psychologist to determine the validity of the score obtained.

Other methods, such as the Bender[9] and the Goodenough Draw-a-Man technique,[22] utilize special psychomotor capacities to obtain levels of mental maturity.

INTERPRETING THE I.Q. SCORE

The intelligence of the United States population is distributed as shown on Table 4. In using this table, it is important to remember that the distribution represents only a rough estimate, and that different intelligence tests vary considerably in the interpretation of the gradations above and below normal. Table 5 illustrates how interpretation of I.Q.s can differ. In general, Table 4 is more applicable to the Stanford–Binet Test, and Table 5 to the Wechsler–Bellevue, Form I.

One of the errors most frequently made by persons attempting to interpret the meaning of I.Q.s is to ignore the local norms of

TABLE 4. DISTRIBUTION AND CLASSIFICATION OF I.Q.s IN TERMAN-MERRILL STANDARDIZATION GROUP*

I.Q. range	Classification	Percent of cases
140 and above	Genius or near genius	1·3
120–140	Very superior intelligence	11·3
110–120	Superior intelligence	18·1
90–110	Normal or average intelligence	46·5
80–90	Dullness	14·5
70–80	Borderline deficiency	5·6
Below 70	Definite feeble-mindedness	2·6

*Adapted from *Psychology and Life* by Ruch, F. L.[54]

the group tested. It is quite possible—and often occurs—that a person whose I.Q. is below average in terms of the national norms finds himself of superior intelligence within his own cultural group. The reverse is also true. Some people are apt to confuse average I.Q. with average college student's I.Q. We know that the average is 100, but the average college student's I.Q. is placed at about 120. Whether a college student with an I.Q. of 120 will do average level work depends on the type of school he is attending and his work habits. Children of the professional class, with an I.Q. of 110, may experience school difficulties because the average child living in this milieu has an I.Q. approximately five points higher than 110. This same child might appear to be

TABLE 5. INTELLIGENCE CLASSIFICATION ACCORDING TO I.Q.—AGES 10–60 (ACTUAL)*

Classification	I.Q. limits	Percent included
Defective	65 and below	2·2
Borderline	66–79	6·7
Dull Normal	80–90	16·1
Average	91–110	50·0
Bright Normal	111–119	16·1
Superior	120–127	6·7
Very Superior	128 and over	2·2

*From *The Measurement of Adult Intelligence* by Wechsler, D.[63]

brilliant in a group of day laborer's children. Thus, a child can change his apparent mental level from the bright to the dull end of the intellectual continuum simply by moving across the city from one kind of neighborhood to another. The same applies to children who move from one part of a country to another part which differs in average I.Q. levels or from city to country.

Table 6 gives the average I.Q. of children according to father's occupation in the United States.

TABLE 6. MEAN I.Q.s (L-M COMPOSITE) ACCORDING TO FATHER'S OCCUPATION*

Father's occupational classification	Chronological ages			
	2–5½	6–9	10–14	15–18
1. Professional	116·2	114·9	117·5	116·4
2. Semi-professional and managerial	112·4	107·3	112·2	116·7
3. Clerical, skilled trades, and retail business	108·0	104·9	107·4	109·6
4. Rural owners	99·1	94·6	92·4	94·3
5. Semi-skilled, minor clerical, minor business	104·3	104·6	103·4	106·7
6. Slightly-skilled	95·1	100·0	100·6	96·2
7. Day Laborers, urban and rural	93·6	96·0	97·2	97·6

*From *Measuring Intelligence* by Terman, L. M. & Merrill, M. A.[60]

We see from Table 6 that intelligence appears to increase progressively with a rise in the social and intellectual level of the father's occupation. This occurs at an early age (two to five and a half years) and remains at the original level. Some minimize cultural influences as responsible for the higher I.Q. in children of professional fathers. Others argue that the superior homes of the professional groups exert influence at an early age, and that children from these homes are environmentally conditioned to have higher motivation for learning. They explain the higher I.Q's of children in the professional group by this, rather than by genetic factors. To date, no one can say with certainty which of these points of view is correct. Most psychologists are inclined to ascribe considerable weight to the genetic factor in explaining why children of professional parents obtain higher scores on intelligence tests.

The graph, Fig. 2, shows a distribution of I.Q.s in rural and urban groups. This graph was constructed by using the I.Q.s of 1,940 urban and 940 rural subjects.

Figure 2 shows the mode of urban groups falling between 105–114 intelligence quotient; the mode of the rural group falling between 95–104. It should be noted that this graph was constructed a number of years ago. Nothing later is available, but we wonder whether the increased use of television, radio, and greater cultural opportunity now afforded rural people would make a difference if this study were to be repeated at the present time.

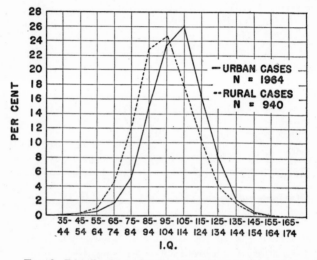

Fig. 2. Distributions of I.Q.s of rural and urban groups.*

Table 7 shows there is a relationship between occupation and the I.Q.s of persons employed in these areas. The I.Q.s shown were computed from the scores of U.S. Army inductees on a general classification test—a specially constructed group intelligence test—used by the U.S. military during World War II. It is important to note the Standard Deviation (S.D.) represents the variability of the scores around the mean, or average. In a normal distribution one S.D. roughly represents 34 percent of the cases that fall on each side of the mean. The one above the mean and

* From *Measuring Intelligence* by Terman, L. M. and Merrill, M. A.[60]

the one below the mean together represent roughly 68 percent of the cases. Now applying this to accountants we see (Table 7) they had a mean I.Q. of 125 and a S.D. of 11. This indicates that 34 percent of this occupational group had from one to eleven

TABLE 7. RELATIONSHIP BETWEEN OCCUPATIONS AND I.Q.s OF PERSONS EMPLOYED IN THESE AREAS*

Occupation	Mean equivalent I.Q.	S.D.
Accountants	125	11
Lawyers	125	10
Engineers	124	11
Teachers	121	12
Stenographers	119	12
Book-keepers	118	12
Clerk-typists	115	11
Radio repairmen	113	13
Receiving and shipping clerks	111	14
Sales clerks	108	14
Auto mechanics	101	15
Painters (general)	98	16
Barbers	95	18
Farm hands	91	18
Teamsters	89	17

*Adapted from *Psychology and Life* by Ruch, F. L.[54]

I.Q. points more than the average and that another 34 percent of this group had up to eleven I.Q. points less than the average. Sixty-eight percent of accountants had I.Q.s ranging from 114 to 136. Let us compare this to farm hands with a mean I.Q. of 91 and a S.D. of 18. This means that 68 percent of this group had I.Q.s ranging from 73 to 109. If we assume the I.Q.s on Table 7 follow a normal distribution and take two or three S.D. from the mean, then a few of the accountants will fall close to the mean I.Q. of farm hands and likewise a few of the I.Q.s of farm hands will fall close to the mean I.Q. of accountants.

Who Should Know a Child's I.Q.?

Some educators make a mystery of the I.Q. Not being certain whether I.Q. is a valid concept, educators are reluctant to

E

broadcast something which appears as final and arbitrary as the mental level of a child. They fear harm to the child, and misinterpretation by the parents. They consider I.Q. to be personal or fear that it will be misinterpreted by the parents. For example, a parent may have felt that his son is capable of going to college and prepare both the child and himself for this. Then he discovers that his son has an I.Q. of 105—a score considerably below the average college level. The parent is torn between his desires to have his son obtain a higher education, and the fear that he will not be able to benefit from it. The boy himself may become quite discouraged and give up his ambitions. The truth is, that this boy might have gone to a university and come through very well. It is never the I.Q. with which one has been endowed, but the amount of native intelligence that one is capable of using that counts. Undoubtedly, with an I.Q. of 105 this boy would have to work harder, and spend more time on his studies. But this does not preclude eventual success in college, provided the youngster with the relatively low I.Q. has a corresponding greater amount of well-directed drive, study habits, and an emotional disposition which permits him to focus on his work. On the other hand, a "genius" with an I.Q. of 150 may be so harrassed by emotional conflicts, or so poorly motivated, that failure in college is a foregone conclusion.

No matter how much intelligence a person has, he can only utilize it fully if he possesses other essential attributes and resources. In order to accomplish a task, do a piece of work, or even gain enough understanding of life to be able to live constructively, one requires besides intelligence the following:

1. Sufficient physical stamina and physiological capacity.
2. Sufficient interest and will to succeed in the enterprise undertaken.
3. Sufficient emotional resources, freedom from conflicts and situational stress to permit full concentration on the task.
4. Sufficient training and preparation for the task to be accomplished.
5. Sufficient resources, tools, money, or equipment.

It is because of these modifying factors that educators attempt to keep children's I.Q.s a secret from their parents. In the opinion of the writers, however, this is not justified. The pediatrician might as well keep the nature of children's illnesses to himself, because knowing the diagnosis might confuse parents. There is no reason why average parents cannot be given the understanding that I.Q. has only limited meaning. Any parent who is capable of comprehending the dangers and complications involved in a case of measles can also understand that an I.Q. must be cautiously interpreted.

Just as parents have the right to know the physical endowments and limitations of their children—as far as medicine and physiology can ascertain them—so do they have the right to know the mental endowments and limitations as far as psychological tests are able to measure them. There is a distinct advantage for parents to know what kind of competition a child is up against in school. Knowing the child's intellectual limitations can help parents plan effectively for the child's future, and assist them in understanding, guiding, and counseling him along the way.

Interpreting Mental Deficiency

The label "mental defective" conjures to the mind of some people a hopeless and immutable fate. The limitations faced by persons found to be mentally defective are real and should not be minimized. However, there are many jobs which persons who are mentally handicapped can perform. Some of these jobs cannot be handled by persons who are too bright because of the monotony involved. Charles[17] has amassed impressive evidence that some children who performed at the imbecile level, later were able to become self-supporting citizens.

Charles describes a group of 206 feeble-minded children who were tested on the Binet in 1916. Their average I.Q. was 60. One hundred and twenty-seven of these were later located and retested. These now ranged from 36 to 49 years in age. It was found that about 65 percent of those who had tested low originally, were now in the dull normal range. Ten percent had risen from the deficient to low borderline level and were able to function as self-sufficient members of society.

The kind of error one may be led to make in evaluating I.Q.s of children who carry the mental defective label is illustrated by one of the test subjects in Charles' study. This individual, with an I.Q. of 50 when tested as a child in 1916, was able to obtain an I.Q. of 84 when tested at the age of 40. Charles describes him as follows:

"H. G. is neat and clean in appearance and pleasant in manner. He is not married and lived with his mother until her death several years ago. Since then he has stayed on in the family home, recently with a married sister and her four-year-old boy. At the time of the interview the home was neat, clean and pleasant. . . . The subject has been employed as a custodian in an industrial plant for the last three years. Before that he sold newspapers and candy at a railroad station. He had small, occasional relief grants . . . and was brought before a juvenile court for a misdemeanor in 1928, but there is no evidence of law breaking since then. The subject's conduct and performance would suggest that the I.Q. score of 84 on the Wechsler is a better index of present level of functioning than the 1916 Binet I.Q. of 50."[17]

This study did not reveal whether the original testing was valid, whether the child was motivated at the time, and to what extent the child was emotionally disturbed when tested. It shows that children may test very low in I.Q. without requiring institutionalization all their lives. We have a debt to the child born defective, as well as to society, to salvage such constructive capacities as we can among our sizeable population of feeble-minded persons. In the United States alone, there are estimated to be approximately 5,000,000 people who have various degrees of mental deficiency.

Capacities and Limitations of Morons, Imbeciles, and Idiots

Morons (I.Q. from 51 to 70). As adults have mental age of 7 to 12 years.

1. Capacities:
   A. Can perform routine factory or farm work.
   B. Can learn to read and write.
   C. Can evolve into self-supporting citizens under favorable environment.

2. Limitations:
   A. Do not usually progress past 5 to 6 years of schooling.
   B. Often incapable of recognizing their moral and legal obligations and therefore apt to become delinquents, prostitutes, and petty thieves when not properly guided.

C. Their physical maturity in the absence of corresponding mental maturity, predisposes to unregulated and sometimes antisocial behavior. For example, in the United States, the frequency of illegitimate motherhood is highest among moron girls.

Imbeciles (I.Q. from 26 to 50). As adults have mental age of 3 to 7 years.

1. Capacities:
   A. Can learn to talk.
   B. Can do simple work under supervision, such as mopping floors, rough painting, digging, and simple farm chores.
   C. If tractable and closely supervised, may possibly be self-supporting.

2. Limitations:
   A. Usually do not understand the value of money.
   B. Usually should not be permitted to live outside of institutions or away from very close supervision of the families.
   C. May be dangerous to self or others when emotionally upset or sexually aroused.

Idiots (I.Q. up to 25). As adults have mental age of 2 years.

1. Capacities:
   A. May learn to eat food without aid.
   B. May make themselves understood by grunts or even a few simple words.
   C. May learn to partially dress themselves.

2. Limitations:
   A. Must be institutionalized to avoid common dangers of life.
   B. Often have poor physical stamina and subject to early demise.
   C. Usually unable to contribute constructively in any task and require constant supervision.

CHAPTER V

METHODS FOR TESTING AND EVALUATING ORGANIC BRAIN IMPAIRMENT

THE clinical psychologist is often confronted with the task of assisting the neurologist and psychiatrist in the diagnosis of organic brain pathology. In general, there are three reasons that account for the frequency of such referrals. First, neurological signs if present are sometimes inconclusive and contradictory. Second, somaticizing neurotics often present symptoms which are not easily distinguished from genuine brain damage. Third, there is an increasing awareness by members of the medical profession of the contributions which the well-trained clinical psychologist can make toward the identification of intracranial lesions.

No matter how adept the clinical psychologist is in the identification of cerebral damage, he represents the last resort in the collection of the evidence required to make a neurological diagnosis. Too often, in small clinics where neurologists are not readily available or where there is a scarcity of EEG machines, psychiatrists are tempted to place a heavy burden of responsibility on psychologists in the evaluation of symptoms for organicity. The present level of efficiency of psychological techniques in identifying brain damage does not warrant this. Yates[68] has systematically evaluated the present state of accuracy of psychological tests designed to identify organic brain damage. In general, he finds them wanting. He suggests employment of new techniques which would yield objective scoring criteria, based on what he calls "a reasonable theory", supported by adequate statistical treatment. In his assessment of available techniques, he did not include the Bender Motor Visual Gestalt Test, the Benton Retention Test, the Revised Babcock Test of Mental Deterioration, and the Kahn Test of Symbol Arrangement.

Tests utilized for identification of organic brain disease share conspicuously in the barrage of criticism which is generally directed at psychological diagnostic instruments by research psychologists. However, psychological methods for the identification of brain damage are becoming more, rather than less, popular among neurosurgeons, neurologists, and psychiatrists. In spite of their shortcomings, and apparent inability to stand up credibly when subjected to statistical analysis, these methods are useful. The authors can recall many cases where psychological testing alerted the attending physician to the presence of an organic-cerebral disease in what appeared to have been a purely functional condition. Follow-up studies proved that the psychological test indications of organic brain disease were correct. Most clinical psychologists in practice for any length of time can give similar examples. It is difficult to say whether or not the tests for brain damage currently in use are inadequate or whether the shoe of inadequacy fits better the statistical techniques used in the assessment of their accuracy.

Psychological tests are employed when presence of organic brain disease has already been established, to assay the extent of loss in cognitive and emotional areas. Before we mention specific signs and indices of loss, it may be fruitful to consider briefly the theories underlying the use of psychological tests in disease involving intracranial lesions.

In an analysis of such theories, there are two considerations. First, the patient with organic brain damage will react psychologically to his pathology in a characteristic manner, which is reflected and identifiable on psychological tests. Second, psychological tests are sensitive to early impairment of cerebral efficiency, and sometimes inability to meaningfully integrate psychological test stimuli (such as the Rorschach blot) precedes the appearance of positive neurological signs. Likewise, some psychological tests in which blocks or designs are used, are sensitive to impairment of the psycho-motor-spacial field; others in the visual and the retentive fields. Performance in these areas can be observed and measured conveniently and accurately by means of psychological tests. Deterioration may be estimated by comparison of performance in other areas of function. This can be accomplished in a relatively objective manner by using hundreds of cases with known damage as an experimental group, and without brain damage as controls. Then any given individual performance can be compared with these results.

Psychological reaction to an organic deficit has some general characteristics shared by large numbers of organic patients. Typically, the brain damaged patient is expected to feel insecure, be rigid in his behavior, perseverate in responses, and be slow in his reactions. Is this behavior due to cortical malfunction, or is it psychological reaction to illness? A case may be made for either side. A patient aware of a loss of skill due to organic deficit is slow to respond to a test situation because the awareness of this loss makes him insecure, hesitant, and cautious. On the other hand, this slowness may be attributed to impaired neural tracts, and weakened capacity for cortical integration. There is much to recommend the point of view that the weakness of the premorbid personality is accentuated among patients whose disease has made inroads in effective cortical functioning. Persons whose psychological homeostasis has been upset by any type of disease are less able to inhibit suppressed emotions, or to effectively act a role in life which serves to disguise their true dynamic selves. This is also true of persons subjected to an increase of purely environmental situational stress and is, therefore, not necessarily confined to brain damaged patients. Other attempts to classify tests of brain damage into "quantitative" and "qualitative" types have failed since such a division is arbitrary, and there is too much overlapping. Perhaps it is most practical instead to divide psychological instruments which measure brain damage into those designed explicitly for this purpose, and those which are primarily personality or intelligence tests. In the latter, the brain damage component is a secondary, though not necessarily a less important function.

TESTS DESIGNED TO MEASURE BRAIN DAMAGE

The Hunt-Minnesota Test for Organic Brain Damage[31]

In the introduction to the test, Hunt writes: "The Hunt-Minnesota Test is specifically designed for routine clinical detection of organic brain damage, primarily where the damage has occurred after the person has reached the age of 14 or 15 years."[31] In many ways this test is typical of a group of techniques that utilize recall of designs, words, and numbers (recent memory) and match this performance against vocabulary or general information representing early memory. An age factor is taken into account and a differential for deterioration is computed. A more detailed list from the Hunt-Minnesota Test follows:

1. Matching of designs.
2. Recall of words.
3. Saying the months of the year.
4. Counting from 1 to 20.
5. Counting from 3 to 30 by 3's.
6. The attention test.

The instructions for the attention test are: "I am going to read a long list of numbers and I want you to tap on the table with this pencil every time I read the number 3. Here is a short list for practice—5, 3, 6, 8, 3, 3. Now, listen carefully and be sure to tap the table every time I say the number 3." Other tasks on the test are:

7. Counting backward from 25 to 1.
8. Reversing digits.
9. Saying the months backwards.
10. Serial subtraction of 3's from 79.

The instructions for the serial subtraction are: "Now, I want you to count backwards from 79 to 1 by 3's as fast as you can. Now you start at 79 and count backward by 3's as fast as you can like this: 79, 76, 73, and so on back to 1. Ready, 79 . . ."

As the reader may recognize, the above is similar to the mental status examination routinely used by physicians. The difference is that here the task is part of a framework of a total recall situation in which it is compared to efficiency on other tasks, and is statistically weighted and scored in accordance with total performance.

The Shipley–Hartford Retreat Scale[56]

This test uses the fact that brain damaged patients deteriorate in their capacity for abstract thinking. Concreteness is a characteristic of the intellectual functioning of organic patients, although it is also seen in other mental pathological conditions. Shipley's test requires the patient to make twenty abstract completions.

Instructions are: "Complete the following. Each dash calls for either a number or a letter to be filled in. Every line represents an item. You have ten minutes to finish."

Examples of this task are:

1. White, black, short, long, down — —.
2. NE/SW SE/NW E/W N/-.
3. Surgeon 1234567 snore 17635 rouge — — — — —.
4. 3124 82 73 154 46 13 —.
5. Two w four r one o three —.

Performance on this task is matched with a multiple choice vocabulary test which is assumed to represent the premorbid level of intellectual functioning. The ratio of abstract to vocabulary performance is developed into a percentage of deterioration score.

Goldstein–Scheerer Tests[21]

Another series which employs the principle of abstract and concrete thinking in the detection of organic brain disease, is commonly referred to as the "Goldstein–Scheerer Tests". The chief difference between these tests and the foregoing we have mentioned, is that Goldstein and Scheerer employed actual objects rather than words or numbers. For example, the Goldstein–Scheerer Cube Test uses four wooden blocks whose surfaces present different colors and color combinations. Two spiral bound books show a series of twelve designs of increasing difficulty which the patient must copy, using the colors on the blocks to make the designs. An ingenious aspect of the test is that the designs not only increase in difficulty as the patient proceeds, but when failure occurs, a series of graduated hints are given. The amount of help required can be used as a quantitative measure of impairment. The type of hint offered may be of interest to the reader. They are as follows:

1. Printed design about one-fourth the size of the final design the patient must reproduce with the blocks.
2. (If he fails above) Printed design exact size of the one patient must reproduce with the blocks.
3. (If the patient fails above) Printed design quarter size, with lines showing how the blocks must be fitted together.
4. (If the patient fails above) Printed design exact size of the one patient must reproduce with blocks. Lines are also present showing how the blocks must be fitted together.

Thus, upon failure the tasks become increasingly less abstract until (4) they represent pure visual-psycho-motor performance without abstraction.

The Weigl–Goldstein–Scheerer Color Form Sorting Test consists of four triangular plastic objects, and a like number of square and round plastic objects. All the objects having similar shape, differ in color. The administration of the test is simple. The patient is told to sort the objects, grouping together those which belong together. He may do this by grouping all similar shapes together, or by placing together all objects having similar colors. No matter how he performs the tasks, he is asked subsequently to "sort them differently", inducing him to shift from a shape to color principle, or vice versa. The authors give a behavioral analysis of performance of this task, describing two approaches: the abstract and the concrete. They point out that in the former, the patient "assumes a conceptual attitude from the very start. He carries out the instructions by volitionally abstracting from various individual sense impressions and orients himself toward a conceptional frame of reference in the category of form or color. " . . . In arranging the materials spatially, the subject will casually 'throw' the forms he chooses in different heaps or 'piles', not being particular about the spatial position of the individual figures within each heap."[21] This is contrasted with concrete performance where patients "with disturbance of cortical function are unable to assume the abstract approach and therefore discharge the task on an exclusively concrete level of responding".[21] The patient with organic brain damage has difficulty in abstracting color or form as a principle of sorting. He shows a preference for one way of grouping the figures and arranges them in designs or patterns as a substitute for abstraction. He is unable to shift volitionally from either color to form or form to color. Goldstein and Scheerer point out that "in so far as shifting occurs, it occurs *passively under forcible* experimental conditions"[21] which the test provides by means of the graduated hints. If the patient perseverates in the use of color, and seems unable to grasp the idea of form, the examiner can turn all the pieces upside-down, and thus reversed they are all white. Since color is no longer evident, it is automatically eliminated as a sorting factor. In addition to being able to shift from color to form, the test requires that the patient account for the principles he used to accomplish the task. Thus, the verbal-cortical areas as well as the psychomotor areas are tapped by this test.

The Goldstein–Scheerer Stick Test consists of thirty sticks of four lengths. The materials are used to determine whether the patient is able to copy figures, composed of sticks, and reproduce them from memory. The test is divided into two parts, the first requiring the patient to copy a sample figure; the second, to reproduce the figure after it has been exposed 5 to 30 seconds and then removed.

The other tests of this series, the Gelb–Goldstein Color Sorting Test and the Goldstein–Scheerer Object Sorting Test, require the patient to make color associations, and in the sorting test, to sort a variety of simultaneously presented objects according to general concepts, and to shift frames of references volitionally and without assistance. Some of the objects used in the sorting test are a hammer, a pair of pliers, a pipe, a book, a pencil, a bicycle bell, matches, and a candle.

The Benton Revised Visual Retention Test[11]

This is an example of tests that rely exclusively on the patient's ability to use visual memory effectively. The evaluation of results are described in detail in Benton's manual. The test can be given in one of four possible administrations or in combination of several administrations. The directions for administration are:

"The subject is given a blank sheet of paper, the dimensions of which correspond to the dimensions of the cards on which the designs are printed, and a pencil with an eraser. He is told that he will be shown a card on which there are one or more figures, that he will study the card for 10 seconds, and that when the card is removed he will draw what he has seen."[11]

Benton suggests both a quantitative and qualitative analysis of performance. The qualitative aspect is measured largely by the amount and kind of distortion, such as reversal, rotation of figures, and the general fidelity of the reproductions. The quantitative scoring follows the usual pattern of evaluating such tests. Table 8 indicates the number of errors made by a brain damaged group, and a group of patients who have been screened for an absence of organic brain disease.

TABLE 8. DISTRIBUTION OF PERFORMANCE LEVELS IN BRAIN-INJURED AND CONTROL PATIENTS*

"NUMBER CORRECT" SCORES

Performance level	Brain-injured (N-100)	Control (N-100)
2 points *above* expected level	2	4
1 point ,, ,, ,,	4	17
Equal to ,, ,,	9	34
1 point *below* ,, ,,	16	29
2 points ,, ,, ,,	12	12
3 ,, ,, ,, ,,	21	4
4 ,, ,, ,, ,,	12	—
5 ,, ,, ,, ,,	13	—
6 ,, ,, ,, ,,	7	—
7 ,, ,, ,, ,,	3	—
8 ,, ,, ,, ,,	1	—
	100	100

*From *The Revised Retention Test* by Benton, A. L.[11]

Benton's test is of greatest value in distinguishing brain damage from non-brain damage groups where performance falls four points below expected levels. One of the designs used on the Benton Test is shown in Fig. 3.

The Grassi Block Substitution Test[24]

Grassi requires the patient to make copies of a set of blocks. The models are presented to the patient at four levels of increasing

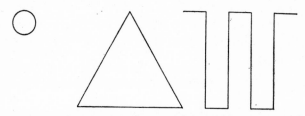

FIG. 3. Sample of the Benton designs.*

* Adapted from *The Revised Visual Retention Test* by Benton, A. L.[11]

complexity. These range from the simple concrete task, in which the patient copies only the top side of the model, to the complex concrete task where the patient has to copy the model correctly with respect to all six sides. He must produce it in a different color schema.

TESTS FOR SPECIFIC CEREBRAL CONDITIONS

Aphasia, Agnosia, and Apraxia

Eisenson's[20] technique is the most comprehensive and popular psychological method for examining for presence of aphasia and associated disorders. In his manual, he describes the nature of congenital and acquired aphasia, as well as areas of disturbance and testing for intellectual changes. The materials in Eisenson's tests are a set of pictures, colors, geometric forms and selected verbal items. Additionally, a kit is furnished consisting of such materials as a penknife, a teaspoon, a key, shoelace, comb, scissors, and a clock face with easily moveable hands. The test is constructed for both screening and diagnosis. Evaluation of the following pathological conditions is possible:

1. Primarily for evaluative and receptive disturbance.
   (a) Visual agnosia: recognition of common objects, pictures, colors, forms, numbers, letters, printed words, and printed sentences.
   (b) Auditory agnosia: recognition of sounds such as coughing, humming, whistling, clapping and word identification.
   (c) Tactile agnosia: object identification while blindfolded, using left and right hand.
   (d) Auditory-verbal aphasia: verbal comprehension, oral sentences, reading comprehension, oral paragraphs.
   (e) Silent-verbal aphasia: silent reading comprehension.

2. Predominantly productive and expressive disturbances.
   (a) Non-verbal apraxia: body parts, simple skills, and pretended action.
   (b) Verbal apraxia: numbers, words, and sentences.
   (c) Automatic speech-counting: recitation of various types, singing.

(d) Writing: numbers and letters, spelling, naming, word finding, arithmetic processes, and oral reading.

(e) Time recognition: clock setting.

In Eisenson's test, all areas are scored as to extent of loss in the following manner: complete, severe, moderate, little or none.

A shorter method for the examination of agnosia, apraxia, and aphasia is offered in the *Mental Examiners' Handbook*.[66]

Basically, the method used here is similar to the longer and more thorough Eisenson technique. Again we have naming objects, repetition of spoken words, writing from dictation, complicated actions (testing for ideational apraxia), tactile recognition of objects, plus special tests for agraphia, alexia, and Parkinson's disease. Furthermore, the authors have offered a method for estimating percentage of loss, although no data are given to show the validity or reliability of such an estimate. Loss in each area is computed by the percentage of answers which the patient failed.

Another approach which claims to do no more than a rough screening was designed by Kahn. Known as the Kahn Apraxia Test, KAT,* the method consists of a single sheet of twenty questions. The same materials used on the Kahn Test of Symbol Arrangement are employed. The test does not attempt to measure the finer differentiations of these disease entities, but merely to detect their presence, and roughly estimate the percentage of loss. Because the test is non-specific, and too short for validity, it should not be used alone when there is reason to suspect any of the fore-mentioned conditions. The KAT was developed primarily as a quick and convenient screening method. As such it has proven useful in alerting the psychologist to the possible presence of an organic condition and to the need of a more thorough investigation of the patient's symptoms.

DETERMINING CEREBRAL DOMINANCE

The Harris Test of Lateral Dominance[26]

This is used in speech and reading clinics for cases where lateral dominance may be a factor, and for preschool age groups with motor handicaps. The test is applicable to ages six and over, and

* This test is in the experimental stage.

yields thirteen scores to determine which hemisphere is dominant. These are:

1 and 2. Knowledge of left- and right-hand performance
3. Simultaneous writing
4. Handwriting
5. Tapping
6. Dealing cards
7. Strength of grip
8. Total hand dominance
9. Monocular sighting
10. Binocular sighting
11. Visual acuity
12. Total eye dominance
13. Kicking

Peacher writes: "It is conceivable that this test (Harris Test of Lateral Dominance) might also be of value in the determination of laterality in cerebral lesions in adults with aphasia. This would concern the case of pathology in Broca's area in right-handed individuals in the absence of aphasia. Detailed testing, by revealing that such an individual may actually be predominantly left-handed, may obviate the production of aphasia in the anticipated dominant hemisphere."[48]

The A-B-C Vision Test for Ocular Dominance[42]

This test was designed by Walter R. Miles and is applicable to ages 5 and over. The apparatus requires simultaneous and balanced use of the hands, and gives the test subject the impression that he is using both eyes, when in actuality he is employing unilateral sighting. It is considered to be the "most satisfactory single test of ocular dominance presently available".[61] Materials include three V-Scopes, ten area-blackness-comparison cards, and instructions for the examinee.

TESTS PRIMARILY DESIGNED FOR THE ASSESSMENT

OF PERSONALITY OR INTELLIGENCE

The foregoing tests were designed specifically for the evaluation of organic conditions. The tests that follow are used just as frequently for determination of organic brain pathology, although their general function is a much broader one. The fact that they are not confined to any specific disease entity makes them in some respect more useful because they suggest other diagnostic categories, in the event that organic pathology is ruled out. It is unlikely that a psychological method can identify only behavior due to cortical or motor neural tract deficiency without being sensitive to general personality characteristics.

The Bender Visual Motor Gestalt Test[9]

This is a popular inclusion in the organic battery. Lauretta Bender devotes two chapters of her book to the test and its use in clinical consideration of organic factors. These deal with:

1. Sensory aphasia and cerebral localization of the visual motor gestalt functions.
2. The disturbance in visual motor gestalten in different types of organic brain disease.

Although the author describes responses typical of other conditions such as schizophrenia, manic depressive psychosis, mental defectiveness, and psychoneuroses, the test's greatest usefulness remains in the field of organic assessment, and in the evaluation of developmental motor maturity levels. The materials consist of eight cards, each one presenting a geometric design which the patient is asked to copy. Many psychologists simply have the patient reproduce the figures as he sees them on the card. Others require the patient to draw the figures from memory after a time lag. Figure 4 shows the designs as they appear on the cards. Nine of the designs are taken from Wertheimer's original patterns used by him for research in visual gestalt psychology.[67]

In her discussion of dementia paralytica, Bender describes how patients with this condition are apt to make their figures very small, to fragment and separate parts. This is found associated with various diseases of the brain, and occurs as a result of weakening or poverty of impulses. In cases where there is not much evidence of pathology, and intelligence remains intact, there are tendencies to reversion to primitive groups. Such primitivization may be assessed by referring to Fig. 5. It shows what can be expected at various age levels. Regression to an early psychomotor developmental level is found associated with many diseases, functional as well as organic.

Progressive encephalopathy, such as seen in alcoholic psychoses, often shows a tendency to interrupt an incomplete figure by stroke-like perseverations. Patients with traumatic psychoses

F

sometimes produce rather bizarre forms. Disturbance in acute confusional states is reflected in poor integration of parts of the figures as compared to the whole, with some confusion of background. In such cases, primitive regression is secondary to the primary difficulty. When the condition produces lethargy or dullness, micrographia is often noted on the Bender.

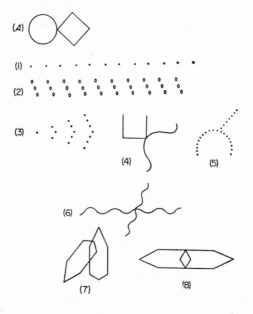

FIG. 4. Test figures adapted from Wertheimer.*

In general, psychologists consider the following as organic signs on the Bender:

1. Serious disturbance of internal gestalt.
2. Primitive features.
3. Modification or substitution of parts of figure.
4. Micrographia or macrographia.
5. Difficulty with angles.
6. Partial rotation (as compared with complete rotation believed to be more typical of schizophrenia).

* From *Instructions for the Use of Visual Motor Gestalt Test* by Bender, Lauretta.[10]

7. Vagueness and sketchiness.
8. Loss of detail and fragmentation.
9. Perseveration, concreteness, overlapping, and over-simplification.
10. Manifestations of need for visual guidance such as using the edge of the paper as a guide, drawing guide lines, especially when associated with impotence and perplexity.

It is usual to find one or more of the above organic signs among patients having brain damage. If only one sign is found, it is

	Fig. A	Fig. I	Fig. 2	Fig. 3	Fig. 4	Fig. 5	Fig. 6	Fig. 7	Fig. 8
Adult	100%	25%	100%	100%	100%	100%	100%	100%	100%
11yrs	95%	95%	65%	60%	95%	90%	70%	75%	90%
10yrs	90%	90%	60%	60%	80%	80%	60%	60%	90%
9yrs	80%	75%	60%	70%	80%	70%	80%	65%	70%
8yrs	75%	75%	75%	60%	80%	65%	70%	65%	65%
7yrs	75%	75%	70%	60%	75%	65%	60%	65%	60%
6yrs	75%	75%	60%	80%	75%	60%	60%	60%	75%
5yrs	85%	85%	60%	80%	70%	60%	60%	60%	75%
4yrs	90%	85%	75%	80%	70%	60%	65%	60%	60%
3yrs				Scribbling					

FIG. 5. Summary of responses for each year of age in developing children. It may be used for evaluating maturational norms and levels of retardation and regression.*

* From *Instructions for the Use of Visual Motor Gestalt Test* by Bender, Lauretta.[10]

usually clearly and strongly manifested. If many signs are present, they may be correspondingly less obvious upon superficial inspection. To illustrate, two patients who were diagnosed as having functional psychoses, when autopsied, showed extensive brain damage. They had previously shown no neurological evidence of this condition. The psychological evaluation of these patients showed evidence strongly suggestive of organic brain disease. Brain sections of these patients demonstrated extensive and diffuse pathology. The patients' performance on the Bender Test elicited unmistakable organic signs. Psychological findings of organic cortical involvement must be taken seriously and, on occasion, psychological signs of organicity may be the only indicators of central nervous system involvement.

The Draw-A-Person Test[41]

The Draw-A-Person Test, or DAP as it is commonly called, simply requires that the patient draw a person. The test subject is free to draw any type of person, male or female. After the completion of the first drawing, he is asked to draw a person of the opposite sex. One of the pioneers in this method of appraisal, Karen Machover, has included in her book on human figures characteristic responses of individuals suspected of organic brain pathology. She considers the following suggestive:

1. Lack of details
2. Erasures infrequent
3. Figures may be large
4. Head large
5. Lines heavy and simple
6. Proportions poor
7. Synthesis weak
8. Omission of parts

It has been found that tests which are easiest to administer are often the most difficult to interpret. These signs, which Machover lists as characteristic of patients with brain lesions, are not easy to distinguish from drawings of some types of neurotics and psychotics. However, if one has had extensive experience with the drawings of various types of clinical groups, one finds that they do follow recognizable patterns, and therefore, to the experienced eye, the DAP has a useful place in the organic battery. This is also true of drawings other than those involving persons as the theme. In general, the art production of patients with organic brain disease show an emptiness with marked absence of detail, and distortion of proportions. Bizarre features, the distinguishing mark of the florid schizophrenic, is seen among patients with organic brain pathology only when psychosis is also present. The brain damaged patient's integration of the parts of the drawing (his so-called gestalt formation) is apt to be weaker than that of the non-organic schizophrenic. (See Chapter III for a discussion of differential diagnosis with psychological tests.)

The Lowenfeld Mosaic Test[38]

The Lowenfeld method of examination was developed in England and is becoming more popular in the United States and other countries. It gets away from the paper and pencil aspect of psychological testing, and allows the patient to work with geometrically shaped, plastic designs of various colors. The literature on the use of this test for organic brain disease is growing, although the test designer's own book remains as the classic in this field. The chapter in the book written by Dr. Henri Ellenberger describes the performance of cases with cerebral arteriosclerosis, cerebral atrophy, cerebral stroke with aphasia, traumatic brain damage, Korsakoff's Syndrome, general paresis, post encephalitic syndromes, and epilepsy. Organic signs on the Lowenfeld test are:

1. Lack of response to the test.
2. Lack of comprehension of test directions (advanced cases).
3. Lack of enjoyment from the test (in contrast to schizophrenics).
4. Irritation by difficulties of the test, often with an expression of dissatisfaction and feelings of having failed.
5. Difficulty and failure in achieving the gestalt the patient has in mind.
6. Selection of a simpler design after failure with the more complicated designs.

Organic signs in the mild forms of the disease:

1. Poorly executed construction of small geometric patterns.
2. Confusion of shapes of test objects. For example, a patient may be constructing a design in which the use of a triangle would complete the picture. Instead, the patient attempts to use a square and does not seem to realize why it fails to fit into the picture.

3. After successful performance in making simple designs, the patient fails when the examiner asks him to make a more complicated design.

4. Insensitivity to variations in color. The patient may make a design using a color that does not fit with the others. He is usually unable to correct this even if the error is called to his attention.

5. An apparently senseless attempt on the part of the patient to keep fitting pieces together in a meaningless manner, regardless of design. Automatic placement with no reference to design suggests the presence of more extensive damage.

A case from Dr. Ellenberger's files illustrates the value of the technique. ". . . Another of our female patients was diagnosed as paranoid schizophrenia. She had the delusion that she possessed a large fortune which the government had stolen from her. Invited to do an L.M.T., the patient said she wanted to make a cross—which, in view of her exalted religious beliefs, did not surprise us. But she could not succeed in arranging the arms of the cross. When she tried to correct what she had done wrong she only succeeded in making it worse. . . . The result of the test led us to suspect that the exalted or paranoid utterance of the patient were nothing more than an empty automatism which concealed an organic affection of the brain. She died of heart failure . . . a few weeks after the test, the autopsy disclosed the existence of generalized brain atrophy, without any focal lesion observable with the naked eye."[38]

The Rorschach

The Rorschach's use as a method for detecting organic brain disease is controversial. Nevertheless, it is used extensively. The authors recall a case where a 40-year-old, single, white male had exhibited his genitals in a theater to a young girl sitting next to him. Psychiatric evaluation and complete social case history delineated an individual who suffered extensively from castration anxiety, feelings of sexual inferiority, impotence, and, in general, was chronically functioning on a schizoid level of adjustment. The manifestation of "exhibitionism" fitted nicely into the picture, and the findings pointed to a diagnosis of character and behavior disorder. Psychological evaluation elicited classical signs of organic brain disease. Following this clue, air studies were performed which outlined a central nervous system lesion.

Bell's book, *Projective Techniques*,[7] lists ten signs of organic brain disease as originally formulated by Piotrowski. These have become known as the "Piotrowski signs" of organic brain damage. Bell describes them as "among the most valuable for clinical diagnosis, although their findings have not been entirely accepted by other experimenters".[7] They have been rephrased so as to be more intelligible to persons not acquainted with Rorschach terminology.

Ten Piotrowski Signs of Organic Brain Disease

1. Number of responses less than fifteen.

2. Response time greater than 60 seconds.

3. Less than two M (human movement responses). More than two M may occur in post-traumatic organics with little personality change.

4. Less than 70 per cent of the responses are of average form level.

5. Less than four popular responses.

6. One or more color naming responses (this is a good sign, but it does overlap with schizophrenics, especially those with deterioration).

7. Perseveration of a response, at least three times without regard to form accuracy (this particular type of perseveration overlaps only with schizophrenics and feeble-minded).

8. Impotence—that is, the subject gives a response he knows is a poor one, but still does not or cannot withdraw it.

9. Perplexity—that is, the subject asks constantly for directions and assurance from the examiner. He asks things like: "Is that the right answer? Did I say the right thing? You see it, don't you?" This may occur persistently throughout the record.

10. Automatic phrases which are illogical and irrelevant to the task. (Certain types of neurotic subjects, especially obsessive-compulsives, will exhibit automatic phrases, but they will be logically placed and pertinent to the testing situation.)

Seven Rorschach Signs of Nonpsychotic Organics—Idiopathic Epileptics[25]

1. Stickiness—that is, a modified perseveration in which the subject changes the location variable and even subtly changes the concept itself. This perseveration is on a higher intellectual level than the organic perseveration and will not fall to a minus form level.

2. Pickiness—that is, a Detail (D) to a Small Detail (Dd) approach, which results in a larger number of responses than in psychotic organics, and is frequently accompanied by good form level.

3. Human Movement responses (M) are outweighed by the sum of color responses (C).

4. Human Movement responses (Ms) are frequently given in contrast to organics and schizophrenics, but many of the Ms are poor form level, and their number actually increases with the amount of dementia involved.

5. Fewer Animal Movement responses (FM) than normals (this may be due to the epileptic's preoccupation with the human body).

6. Responses with Color dominant but Form present (CF) plus Pure Color response (C) is greater than responses with Form dominant but Color present (FC). This sign has a total overlap with psychotics and neurotics, except psychopaths.

7. A staccato flow of interpretation—that is, an unsystematic blocking apparently unrelated to blot or concept variables; uneven sequence of response and reaction times, with intra-card blockings.

The Kahn Test of Symbol Arrangement and Organic Signs

This technique, which utilizes recall ability and capacity to make good space-color-form associations, has been found helpful in identifying patients with organic brain pathology. The test materials include sixteen plastic objects having easily recognized shapes with the exception of one object, vaguely resembling a parrot (see Plate 1). The objects used are: three hearts, three dogs, three stars, an anchor, circle, partial circle, cross, parrot, and two butterflies. Murphy, Bolinger, and Ferriman call this method "a radically new approach to the problem of personality evaluation".[46] In the study they were able to distinguish organically impaired patients from a mixed group by using this test. In another study Kahn reports: "Cutoff scores were established for the four groups in the two studies . . . a cutoff score of —54 would separate 92 percent of the first organic group and 100 percent of the second organic group from all non-brain-damaged subjects in both groups" provided three "normal" subjects over 70 years old (in whom some cortical damage may be suspected on the basis of age) are excluded from the study. In all, over 150 test subjects were involved in this investigation.[32] The following signs are adapted from the test manual:[33]

Nonpsychotic. Slow, careful performance; similarly shaped objects carefully placed together; few slants becoming more frequent with increased pathology. Reversals also appear as pathology increases. Meticulousness in the naming task with many, but usually not all of the objects; pointing out likenesses and differences of objects; difficulty in recognizing transparent butterfly, or in naming circle; high Same-as-Before score; as pathology increases, Naming or Function becomes more prominent on the symbol pattern and intangible abstraction fades out. Presence of bizarre responses suggests involvement of the emotional or cognitive areas; number element usually between 50 and 70.

Psychotic. More slanted and inverted objects than any other group, disorderly arrangement on strip, objects out of segments, overlapping; in severe pathology, two objects may be placed in one segment or objects may be crowded on the strip, or fitted into each other. Usually slow or very slow arrangement time; may have bursts of high speed, practically throwing objects down on strip; prone not to place star on star, or butterfly on butterfly in objects-over task, Arrangement III. More divergencies from norms in Naming and in Recall than any other group; a Number Element above 50 is rare, usually ranging 15–50; D (Naming or Function) is the typical Letter Element with B (No Reason, No Symbolization) and X (Concrete Association) also prominent; the occasional Z (Intangible Abstraction) indicates descent from a former level; seldom names P object as parrot; fails to place similarly-shaped objects together in the arrangements, sorts objects automatically without reference to the meaning of the words printed in the rectangles.

The Kahn Test also provides for an estimate of percentage loss due to deterioration by using the Numerical Element of the symbol pattern in the following formula:

$$\text{Percentage loss of efficiency} = 100 - \frac{\text{Numerical Element} \times 100}{\text{I.Q.}}$$

In other words, if a patient obtains a Numerical Element of 90 and his I.Q. is 120, his loss of efficiency is:

Numerical Element divided by I.Q. = 0·75

0·75 times 100 = 75

100 minus 75 = 25, indicating 25 percent loss.

This method is still largely in an experimental stage.

The Wechsler Bellevue, Form I, and the Wechsler Adult Intelligence Scale

This is a method for identification of both organic brain disease and estimating the percentage of deterioration. Wechsler postulates that some of the sub-tests are not lowered with brain damage and others are. Thereby, a comparison between the sub-tests which hold with those that do not, yields an approximation of the deterioration which pathology has caused.

The Wechsler Bellevue. Percentage of loss based on only one test administration is realized by Wechsler as being precarious.

TABLE 9. HOLD AND DON'T HOLD SUB-TESTS*

HOLD TESTS	
W-B I	WAIS
Information†	Vocabulary
Comprehension	Information
Object Assembly	Object Assembly
Picture Completion	Picture Completion
DON'T HOLD TESTS	
Digit Span	Digit Span
Arithmetic	Similarities
Digit Symbol	Digit Symbol
Block Design	Block Design

*Adapted from *The Measurement and Appraisal of Adult Intelligence* by Wechsler, D.[65]

†Or Vocabulary.

Table 9 shows pattern groupings which appear to be useful in identifying cerebral pathology.

One of the most helpful signs differentiating schizophrenics from organics is that among schizophrenics the block design score is relatively high compared to the patient's scores on the other sub-tests. In the case of brain damage, block design is relatively low when thus compared. The Wechsler Profile, Table 10, gives a further breakdown differentiating organics from other psychiatric entities.

TABLE 10. TYPICAL BRAIN DAMAGE WECHSLER PROFILE*

TABLE OF WEIGHTED SCORES

Equivalent Weighted Score	Information	Comprehension	Digit Span	Arithmetic	Similarities	Vocabulary	Picture Arrangement	Picture Completion	Block Design	Object Assembly	Digit Symbol	Equivalent Weighted Score
	V	V	V	V	V	V	P	P	P	P	P	
18	25	20		14	23–24	41–42	20+		38+			18
17	24	19	17	13	21–22	39–40	20		38	26		17
16	23	18	16	12	20	37–38	19		35–37	25	66–67	16
15	21–22	17		11	19	35–36	18	15	33–34	24	62–65	15
14	20	16	15		17–18	32–34	16–17	14	30–32	23	57–61	14
13	18–19	15	14	10	16	29–31	15	13	28–29	22	53–56	13
12	17	14		9	15	27–28	14	12	25–27	20–21	49–52	12
11	15–16	12–13	13		13–14	25–26	12–13		23–24	19	45–48	11
10	13–14	11	12	8	12	22–24	11	11	20–22	18	41–44	10
9	12	10	11	7	11	20–21	10	10	18–19	17	37–40	9
8	10–11	9			9–10	17–19	9	9	16–17	16	33–36	8
7	9	8	10	6	8	15–16	7–8	8	13–15	14–15	29–32	7
6	7–8	7	9	5	7	12–14	6	7	11–12	13	24–28	6
5	6	5–6			5–6	10–11	5		8–10	12	20–23	5
4	4–5	4	8	4	4	7–9	4	6	6–7	10–11	16–19	4
3	2–3	3	7	3	3	5–6	2–3	5	3–5	9	12–15	3
2	1	2	6		1–2	3–4	1	4	1–2	8	8–11	2
1	0	1		2	0	1–2	0	3	0	7	4–7	1
0		0	5	1		0		2		5–6	0–3	0

V—Verbal Scale.   P—Performance Scale.

– – – – Average midpoint of the scores made by this brain damaged patient.

——— Scores on the individual tests made by this patient.

*Adapted from Wechsler-Bellevue Scale, Record Form I, The Psychological Corporation.

The percentage of deterioration as obtained from the Wechsler is calculated as follows:

Step One W.A.I.S.

SUM OF WEIGHTED SCORES	(1) Information; (2) Vocabulary; (3) Picture Completion; (4) Object Assembly.
MINUS THE SUM OF	(1) Digit Span; (2) Arithmetic; (3) Block design; (4) Digit Symbol.

Example. In an actual case of brain damage the patient obtained weighted scores as follows:

	Information	14
HOLD TESTS	Vocabulary	13
	Picture Completion	10
	Object Assembly	8
	SUM	45

	Digit Span	4
DON'T HOLD TESTS	Arithmetic	8
	Block Design	6
	Digit Symbol	9
	SUM	27

Then: 45—27 = 18.

Step Two

The HOLD minus DON'T HOLD score is then divided by the HOLD scores,
Divide 18 by 45 = 0·31 or 31 percent loss of function.
A correction factor for age must be considered and is computed in step 3.

Step Three (Correction Factor-adapted from Wechsler)

The test score utilized was of a 36-year-old patient.

AGE	CORRECTION
20–24	0
25–29	1
30–34	3
35–39	5
40–44	8
45–49	11
50–54	14
55–59	16

Subtracting the correction factor of 5 from 31 percent equals 26 percent loss.

According to the formula for calculating deterioration, the patient has sustained a significant loss of function amounting to approximately 26 percent of his former level. Most psychologists allow a margin of 10 percent error. Even with this allowance, the loss would appear to be significant.

For practical purposes, the loss of function must be translated into usable language. To merely state that the patient has a loss in digit symbol capacity means little to the referring physician. Since this measures the ability to acquire new learning, it becomes more meaningful when translated into these terms: loss of ability to acquire new learning, especially of the psychomotor variety.

Translation of Wechsler Sub-test Terms

INFORMATION — Memory of distant events, education, cultural interests, and opportunities.

COMPREHENSION — Judgment, interest in social conformity, awareness of reality problems, social awareness.

DIGIT SPAN — Immediate recall. Easily affected by anxiety as well as by cerebral damage.

ARITHMETIC — Ability to concentrate, mental alertness, capacity for organization of stimuli.

SIMILARITIES — Verbal concept formation, capacity for verbal abstraction.

VOCABULARY	Education, best single test of general verbal intelligence, recall of old memories.
PICTURE ARRANGEMENT	Sophistication, ability to anticipate initial acts or situations.
PICTURE COMPLETION	Alertness, ability to differentiate essential from non-essential.
BLOCK DESIGN	This is among the most vulnerable sub-tests to the inroads of cerebral pathology of many types. Represents visual-motor co-ordination and space orientation.
OBJECT ASSEMBLY	Capacity for visual motor organization combined with past memory or habit formation. Because it draws on early memory it is used as a "Hold" test in contrast with "digit symbol" where early memory plays no role.
DIGIT SYMBOL	Capacity for new learning, visual motor activity and efficiency of routine psycho-motor functioning.

For further details of personality variables from Wechsler sub-scores see Table 1.

Psychological tests are an important adjunct to the examination of patients suspected of having cerebral pathology. Their use, however, is justified only in conjunction with neurological and psychiatric examinations. When medical examinations are inconclusive, with borderline signs, contradictory clinical manifestations, or overlapping symptomatology, psychological tests can be useful. They effect the decision of the physician in performing further diagnostic procedures.

Of far greater scientific accuracy is the use of psychological instruments for measuring the amount of mental and intellectual deterioration which has occurred in patients with known cerebral disease and trauma. The increased use of psychological tests for assessment of intellectual loss and emotional changes is recommended.

CHAPTER VI

IDENTIFICATION OF SCHIZOPHRENIA

FEW medical entities have been subject to more speculation and controversy than the diagnostic category generally referred to as schizophrenia. Without considering the etiology, physiological or psychological factors that are involved in the genesis and development of the condition, we are faced with a recognizable behavioral syndrome. It is the presence of this syndrome which the psychologist attempts to probe by means of his tests. Accordingly, Kahn writes: ". . . we are limiting ourselves to the consideration of the behavior which earned our patients their diagnostic titles; not with the nature of their disease. It may be that the term schizophrenia exists only in the mind of the psychiatrists who made the diagnoses. By schizophrenia, we mean the behavior which caused these psychiatrists to apply the term in their clinical appraisals."[33]

It follows that psychological testing in cases where schizophrenia is suspected, attempts to elicit test behavior that corresponds with schizophrenic symptoms; that is delusions, hallucinations, and paranoid ideation, as well as the more subtle manifestations of increased rigidity, concreteness, autism, depersonalization, and loosening of anchorage to reality. In schizophrenia, as in other mental disease entities, the premorbid behavior in life is often artificially sustained by habits, and circumscribed by conventional surroundings, to the extent that the clinical manifestations are repressed, internalized, sublimated, or disguised, making them difficult to recognize. Some patients develop acute symptoms upon admission to the hospital, where they can "let go" and be their "psychotic selves". Others, with greater "holding-on" powers, may not manifest their psychopathology until confronted with a psychological test situation. Testing creates a new situation, and, in addition, it constitutes a stress situation. It is devoid of familiar sounds, sights, and motions which help the individual maintain his premorbid equilibrium.

Apart from the obvious fact that testing gives the psychiatrist objective confirmation of his clinical judgment, we have many borderline cases where the psychotic process is in a prodromal or incipient state. In these cases, testing often elicits signs of the disease in advance of more readily assessable symptomatology. Furthermore, there is the difficult problem of overlapping symptoms in which the patient's behavior could easily fit into a number of different clinical conditions. While talking of genuine schizophrenia—whatever that may be—we must not forget the pseudo-schizophrenic-neurotics, and the pseudoneurotic-schizophrenics who present difficult diagnostic problems. Finally, the psychiatrist who wishes to know all he can about the etiology of the condition, the psychodynamics involved, the extent of deterioration caused by the pathology, the islands of strength remaining, and the prognosis, can utilize psychological testing to assist in obtaining this information.

Tests used for the evaluation of schizophrenia are myriad. In the limited treatment of this book, we are able to illustrate only a few techniques utilized in testing for schizophrenia. The tests to be described are: the Rorschach, the Thematic Apperception Test, the Bender Test, the Kahn Test of Symbol Arrangement, the Draw-A-Person Test, the Mosaic Test, and the Wechsler.

THE RORSCHACH TECHNIQUE

Although *Psychodiagnostik* by Hermann Rorschach[53] appeared in 1921, not much work was done with the Rorschach method in the field of schizophrenia until 1935. At this time a number of papers appeared in which the test was used to help determine whether or not schizophrenia was an accentuation of the normal schizothymic type of personality, or an actual disease process provoking qualitative changes in the personality. Various investigators noted that one of the most striking changes found among schizophrenics was a decrease of human movement responses, and a corresponding increase in responses approaching pure color.

It must be clear to anyone working in the field of mental health, that the psychiatric classification of various schizophrenic processes leaves much to be desired. Pure entities of clinical schizophrenia are rare. Often, cases show admixture of hebephrenic,

PLATE 2

This stylized, diagrammatic drawing by a schizophrenic patient
illustrates the chaotic symbolism characteristic of some forms of
the disease.

catatonic, and paranoid syndromes, and may have affective or psychoneurotic coloring. Since clinical behavior patterns labelled schizophrenia are tremendously varied, rarely will a single personality picture typical of schizophrenia emerge on the Rorschach. There are, however, a few signs which seem to be almost pathognomic of the schizophrenic process; there are combinations which tend to point to such a diagnosis. Few cases will present all of the signs; many will present only a few. Each case must be evaluated separately, and the number and value of the schizophrenic signs must be carefully weighed. The psychologist must seek corroborating evidence on other tests used in the psychological battery.

Specific Rorschach Indicators of Schizophrenia

The following Rorschach signs for schizophrenia are given, and the necessary cautions are added to show that careful evaluation is required, even in the interpretation of the pathognomic signs.

Deviant verbalization. Example: Card I. "Man carrying a bag of frogs in the desert." Cautions: The examiner must be alert to factors which would influence a patient in deviating from the general run of the normal population. Malingering must also be ruled out. Therefore, inquiry into the background of the deviant verbalization is required.

Confabulation. Illogical expansion of perceived concept. Example: The whole of Card IX is, "a bear, because I see claws here". (In the lower third of the card—upper pink area.)

Fabulation (contamination). Arbitrary combinations of concepts. Such combinations are not seen in nature and are made only because of the spacial positions on the blots, or because of colors. Example: Card VII. "Two rabbits sitting on a large butterfly." Two rabbits are seen in the top half of the blot; a butterfly is seen on the bottom half. The two concepts are combined by the test subject because they are adjacent. Cautions: This is sometimes seen among obsessive-compulsives. Card I. "Bat-woman" because "the card looks like a bat and also looks like a woman—therefore, it is a bat-woman". Card X. "A caterpillar crawling in the grass, caterpillar because of its shape, and it is on the grass because it is green." Caution: Sometimes seen among schizoids and hysterics.

Projected inferences. This includes assigning emotional or
G

threatening characteristics to the conceptualizations. Example: Card VIII. "A beast of prey ready to tear you to pieces." Card VII. "Two women—one laughing and the other one crying because she can't stand being laughed at." Caution: This sign sometimes occurs among paranoid personalities of the character and behavior type. Also seen among some normals who wish to share or divulge their dynamics to the examiner.

Perseveration. Automatic repetitions. Example: Card I. "Bat." Card II. "Bat." Card III. "Bat." Caution: Sometimes seen in organic brain disease.

Summary and Discussion of Important Rorschach Signs

A study of the signs shows that the interpretation of a record and its evaluation for schizophrenia, requires more than a mechanical approach to the task. The intensity of the sign is a very important consideration. For example, on Card VII, it makes a difference whether the patient sees the "two women" as being jealous of each other—a relatively benign form of projective inference—or whether he sees these figures as "planning to exterminate each other", which is obviously more pathological. Likewise, a "rabbit's head" (lower center of Card X) "with green tears coming out of his eyes", is a less pathological combination than "A rabbit's head with green snakes devouring the rabbit's eyes". In the latter response, a projective inference is added to the fabulation. The impression of schizophrenia is more solidly supported when signs are strongly and persistently manifested on the record.

Less Specific Rorschach Indicators of Schizophrenia

Poor form conceptions. Example: Card V. "A piece of cloth." Card III. "A chair." Caution: Also seen among patients with brain damage, malingerers, and extremely hostile patients. The patient may suffer from visual difficulties.

Pure color responses. Exclusive or predominant use of color in the formation of concepts, including a mere naming of the colors on the cards. Example: "red paint", "grass because it is green". Caution: These signs are seen in organic brain disease, and among hysterical personalities.

Few or no human movement responses. Example: Card III. "Two chickens." Caution: Paranoid and "over-ideational schizophrenics" often have more than the average number of human responses. This is one of the means for differentiating paranoid schizophrenics from the more obvious forms of the disease.

Rejections. Schizophrenics sometimes reject two, three, and more of the cards, saying that they see "nothing", "can't make out anything". Caution: Rejection of cards also occurs among emotionally blocked hysterics, hostile persons with character disorders. It is also seen among malingerers and normals who resent the test situation, and neurotics who are overwhelmed by the anxiety-provoking aspects of the stimulus materials.

Variability. Shifts from good form to poor form or vice versa. Variation in reaction time. Variability must be extreme before this becomes a good sign; 2 or 3 seconds on one card and over 40 seconds on another cards. Form fidelity must range from very good to quite poor. If the record is long, allowance must be made for a corresponding increase in variability, in regard to form and reaction time. Caution: Anxiety neurotics are sometimes variable in their response patterns because they find some of the cards, notably those with color, more threatening. Thus, a long delay in response to a non-colored card is more suggestive of severe pathology.

Differential Diagnosis on the Rorschach

Hebephrenic Schizophrenia—Response Pattern

1. Numerous poor form responses.
2. Absence of shading, such as "fur", "texture".
3. Bizarre or "explosive" responses: "something breaking up", "a piece of dirt falling down", "oh, look at Dippy Do eating his pie".
4. Fixed concept perseveration.
5. Negativism, blocking, occasionally white card area responses. Record not as constricted as seen in catatonics.
6. Color emphasis.

Catatonics—Response Pattern

1. Restricted in withdrawn states of the disease and drawn out in catatonic excitement states.
2. Bizarre, explosive.
3. Usually no shading.
4. Color naming.

5. Blocking more severe than in hebephrenics.
6. Fewer signs of regression than in some other forms of schizophrenia. Such responses as "eating something", "babies", "excreta", are usually absent.

Simple Schizophrenia—Response Pattern

1. Usually less than twelve responses.
2. No human movement, color, or shading; perhaps a few pure color concepts.
3. One or more absurd form responses.
4. High animal content.
5. Perseveration.
6. The relative *absence* of bizarre responses differentiates this form of the disease from the more florid forms of schizophrenia.

Paranoid Schizophrenia—Response Pattern

Because much of the personality structure remains intact in this insidious disease, evidence must be discerned and weighed with special care. Recognition of the condition by psychologists depends on careful assessment of projected grandiose or persecutory delusions. Caution: Paranoid schizophrenics will sometimes attempt to avoid projecting their delusions and, not knowing how to handle the cards without projection, will refuse to take the test. Among the signs sometimes encountered are:

1. Usually one or more deviant verbalizations in which an animal or person seen on the cards will harm some other animal or person. "An eagle swooping down to kill something", "A witch about to sacrifice a baby".
2. Projection of homosexual impulses or attributes. "That man with the moustache (Card IX) has a homosexual look."
3. Emphasis on eyes and mouths in the absence of other good responses. "Two eyes are staring in this card."
4. Usually less than twenty responses with occasionally only four or five responses.
5. One or more contaminations and confabulations.
6. Usually human movement (more than any other schizophrenic group).

THEMATIC APPERCEPTION TEST

Schizophrenics who may be evasive or hostile on the Rorschach because they find the stimulus materials too threatening, often react more favorably to the drawings of the Thematic Apperception Test (TAT) by Murray.[44] This technique is intended for use with individuals 7 years or older. It represents one of many methods in which drawings are utilized to elicit projections. The test subject is asked to tell a story about a picture.

Specific TAT Indicators of Schizophrenia

Rigidity and concreteness. The patient relates only what is obvious in the picture. Refuses to elaborate. "Just a man and a woman there."

Negation. "I see nothing, except a drawing." "I'd rather not tell you."

Perseveration. The patient has a concept which may be relevant to one card. He carries it through inappropriately to other card situations.

Déjà vu reaction. The cards seem to show patients a situation in which he feels familiar, or he recognizes the persons depicted in the drawings.

Projection of homosexual attributes. In paranoid schizophrenia, there is often a projection of homosexual intentions or fears; statements as, "The old woman is scheming a homosexual act with the young one" (Card 12F). Such projections may also be found among non-psychotics with homosexual wishes or fears. Schizophrenics often perseverate and are inappropriate in their projections of homosexual intentions on to the figures in the drawings. Psychotics may use an accusing voice when indicating homosexual intentions, or they may indicate these intentions with a knowing look, revealing their feeling of omniscience.

Projection of threatening or evil intentions, or of exaggerated fears. This sign applies primarily to cards where such projections would be inappropriate or far-fetched. For example: "She is going to kill the other person", is not necessarily a psychotic response for Card 18GF, but it would be for Card 4. Likewise, concepts involving death and destruction are not necessarily psychotic when elicited on Card 15, but when such projections are made inappropriately on Card 13G, they are suggestive of psychosis. This is especially true if they have a bizarre quality and if there is nothing in the patient's recent background—death in the family or some other calamity—to induce such thoughts.

A grossly disproportionate emphasis on relatively insignificant factors in the drawings. Example: The necktie on Card 18BM, the books on Card 13MF, the handkerchief on Card 6GF, and similar small details on the other cards.

Blandness and flattened effect. This is manifested in schizophrenia by complete lack of anxiety in reaction and description of the normally anxiety provoking cards, 18GF, 13MF, 18BM, 3BM, and 3GF.

Frequent or prolonged perusal of the back of the cards. This suggests the presence of paranoid ideation.

Very prolonged reaction time: one or two minutes or more per card. This sign becomes more significant of schizophrenia (as differentiated from depressive psychosis) if there is considerable variation in the reaction time in responding to the series of cards.

The Bender

Schizophrenia is manifested on the Bender primarily by disassociations, spatial separations, and tendencies of gestalt exaggeration. In florid forms of schizophrenia, there are often gross distortions, with primitive scribbling and immature looking picture drawings. Among well preserved paranoid schizophrenics, there is sometimes an exaggerated meticulousness, and variation from the original drawings in regard to size or position. The authors have seen several cases where the patient used a separate sheet of paper for each design. In these cases, the designs were usually drawn two or more times their actual size, corresponding with the patient's inflated and unrealistic self-image. Except for these cases, our experience supports Bender's own summary:

"In the visual motor gestalt function in schizophrenia, therefore, we find the fundamental disturbance of splitting expressing itself by dissociation in the gestalt figures which often distorts them fundamentally so that the gestalt principles are split . . . there is also failure to dissociate functions which tend to stick too closely together so that the experiences of the personality may be represented by any unwieldly conglomeration."[9]

THE KAHN TEST OF SYMBOL ARRANGEMENT (KTSA)

Since schizophrenia is a disturbance in human communication resulting from a distortion of symbolic thinking, a test which probes the capacity for making abstractions with cultural symbols offers a means for identifying the disease. Signs of schizophrenia on this test are relatively clear-cut.

KTSA Indicators of Psychosis

1. Number element of 50 or below. Exceptions: malingerers and mental defectives.
2. "A" in the first four letters of the letter element.
3. Very slow arrangements (110 seconds or more).
4. Twenty or more objects slanted or inverted. Exceptions: malingerers, persons with considerable hostility toward testing, and persons who are visually or physically handicapped.
5. Placing of more than one object in each segment.
6. More than three errors in naming the objects.
7. Twelve or more errors in recalling the position of objects as placed in a previous arrangement. Exceptions: mental defectives and malingerers.
8. More than four objects placed in (in the sorting of objects task): HATE, BAD, or DEAD.

We can add the following new signs which have been found to be suggestive of borderline schizophrenia.

1. One or more "A" responses in combination with nine or more "Z" responses.
2. Perseveration of weak or borderline "Z" responses. Example: Heart, "good luck"; dogs, "good luck too, since having dogs brings a person good luck"; cross, "good luck, because anyone believing in religion is lucky".
3. Refusal to place more than two or three objects in the sorting task.
4. Hostility and suspiciousness against the test and the examiner, especially after the test subject has taken other tests without showing these characteristics. This is because schizophrenics

who use avoidance as a defense, find the dual aspects of the KTSA (verbal and manipulative) to be a double threat, in contrast with tests restricted to one plane of performance. Sometimes schizophrenics with insight and "holding-on" capacities may lavish praise of the test as a reaction formation to this hostility.

5. Exceptional difficulty in placement of one or two objects (exception, the "P" object), frequent changes in position after placing, difficulty in sorting, and an "A" response to the object.

6. Prolonged reaction time to the first arrangement, with the placement of objects first on the table, and exaggerated meticulousness and care in the arrangement of the objects on the strip.

7. One or more objects placed in HATE, BAD, or DEAD, when the patient is unable to give a logical explanation for such placement, is a weak sign. The more objects placed in any of these categories during the sorting task, the stronger the sign, especially if a rational explanation for such placement cannot be elicited.

8. Holding one of the objects in the fist of the hand and showing reluctance in placing it on the strip. Putting an object to the lips, or any other "magical" symbolic gestures with the objects.

9. Meticulous description of objects in the naming task, such as: "A little red heart, approximately the size of a penny, half the size of the blue heart, and about one-quarter inch thick." This sign becomes stronger if the patient also gives similar descriptions during the symbolizing task.

10. Gross verbal-motor inconsistencies: This includes denial of dislike of objects in Arrangement IV, yet placing some in the HATE category in sorting. Judging that nearly all of the objects were placed right or wrong, in Arrangement III, when actually the reverse is true. Giving a "B" (No Reason) response for the arrangements, when there is obviously an arrangement based on color or form.

In general it has been found that schizophrenics have fewer "Z" responses than neurotics (Exception: paranoid schizophrenics); more objects slanted than normals, but less than organics; the highest number of "A" responses of all clinical groups. In contrast with organically damaged patients, the schizophrenic is able to place similarly shaped objects together. In borderline and paranoid schizophrenia, the recall capacity (Arrangement III) often remains high, and there are no errors in naming. The number and type of errors made in the naming task is a rough index of the extent of the deterioration caused by the psychotic process. Psychosis is indicated if the symbol pattern is below 50, except in paranoid or borderline cases. After psychosis has been established, the best means of differential diagnosis with the KTSA requires the use of the table on pages 154-155 in the KTSA manual.[33]

DRAW-A-PERSON TEST

The Draw-A-Person Test (DAP)[41] is in many ways the easiest to administer and the most difficult to interpret. Some persons rely on their book knowledge to ascribe a "one to one" relationship between such things as buttons (dependency needs) and much hair (sexuality). This is misleading and should be avoided.

Although the DAP is, without question, one of the least valid tests when unsupported by other evidence, it is still a useful tool in the hands of well-trained psychologists who do not jump to effortless conclusions, and use the DAP in conjunction with other tests.

Indicators of Schizophrenia from the DAP Test

1. Omission of important parts such as arms, hands, legs, and head.

2. Bizarre additions, such as internal organs, and scribbling which is not appropriate to the drawing.

3. Grossly exaggerated size or emphasis of any part of the drawing, such as the ears, nose, and especially the eyes.

4. Front-view profile confusion of face, such as two eyes or mouth and nose centrally placed in a profile drawing.

5. The presence of sexual organs in the drawings—especially when the rest of the body is dressed or partly dressed.

6. Tiny, empty drawings in the regressed forms of schizophrenia, large drawings with heavy line emphasis in the grandiose and florid types of the disease.

7. A quality of remoteness and social distance in the drawing which is difficult to define. This is usually accompanied with a subtle bizarre coloration. The figure of the nun shown in Plate 3 is an example of this.

In addition to these signs which have been found to be most characteristic of schizophrenia, Karen Machover mentions others: joint emphasis in the simple kind of schizophrenia, rigidity in the paranoid types, erasures infrequent in the regressed types, and a "diagrammatic quality and blocked movement".[41]

THE MOSAIC TEST

Margaret Lowenfeld[38] points out that the diagnostic potential of her Mosaic Test stems from the test's capacity to elicit what she calls the typical schizophrenic symptom—indifference to gestalt. This test enables the psychologist to compare the patient's drawing with his constructions on the mosaic tray. Lowenfeld describes the difference in the case of a schizophrenic woman as follows:

". . . we asked her to draw a cat and she draws a cat that is recognizable, and among other details, possesses four paws. Comparing the mosaic and the drawing we find that a patient, who is perfectly able to draw a cat, makes a mosaic cat which resembles anything but a cat; that she knows this perfectly, but does not mind it in the least."[38]

It appears, then, that some schizophrenics create conceptual designs which are not reality bound, in contrast with the greater reality awareness expressed by the patient when dealing with the more conventional materials of paper and pencil. As with the Kahn Test of Symbol Arrangement, the patient must manipulate individual, solid objects which are combined into a symbolic expression, and thus a level of organizational capacity is tapped. The KTSA and Mosaic Tests require the "bit-by-bit" construction of a gestalt, whereas such tests as the Rorschach and the Thematic Apperception Tests confront the patient with a gestalt that is already present for him to accept or reject. The KTSA utilizes culturally formed symbols, each one of which represents a gestalt in itself. The Mosaic is a more naked medium than the KTSA, since the geometric designs offer no hint as to meaning, and have no identification with anything except abstract designs. We agree with Lowenfeld's statement that, "It is in the study of schizophrenia that the L.M.T. (Lowenfeld Mosaic Test) has yielded by far the most interesting results."[38]

PLATE 3

These drawings show different responses of four male patients who
were asked to draw a person. The male drawings reflect characterological disorders. One represents aggressiveness and over-
confidence; the other helplessness and inadequacy. The female
figures are the work of schizophrenics. One shows repression; the
other loss of all inhibitory capacity.

PLATE 4

This design, produced by a six-year-old female child with the Lowenfeld Mosaic Test, illustrates full use of the board and maximum employment of different colors and shapes. The work represents free and unhampered use of emotional resources together with weakness in self-control and immature judgment.

Indicators of Schizophrenia on the Lowenfeld Test

1. Preoccupation with symmetry and formal organization of the pieces with no attempt to construct any objects commonly seen in life.

2. Color is either over- or under-emphasized; or used unrealistically.

Lowenfeld cautions that these signs are not pathognomic. Instead, the test is best used in the investigation of patients whose diagnosis is already known. The Lowenfeld Test makes its greatest contribution in measuring the degree of disorganization. Four levels of performance are given to indicate this:*

1. *Lowest level.* Corresponds to performance of infants, 16 or 18 months of age. Patient looks at the pieces individually, turns them about in his hand, plays with them, may hold them up to the light, and occasionally may drop one on the tray with no attempt at placing the pieces to form anything.

2. *One level above lowest level.* These patients can place objects on the tray, but make no effort at organization; no choice of color; no constructive use of figures.

3. *Two levels above the lowest level.* Some fragmentary organization is achieved by patients at this level, as manifested by placing the pieces in twos or in a chain across the tray. The performance of these patients can best be described as automatic. Usually they react with very little, if any hesitation, and perform quickly and mechanically. Occasionally, there are some who respond with exaggerated care, slowly and meticulously placing the objects in a straight line or a curve. Slow reaction, such as this, is much more frequent among patients whose disorganization is due to brain damage.

4. *Three levels above the lowest level.* These patients organize the pieces without fragmentation, but with a compulsion for making diagrammatic and formalistic designs. Diamond shapes, hexagons, squares, or triangles are common among this group. In contrast to the preceding level, there are no loose ends. Their performance is differentiated from that of normals by the rigidity of the designs, over-emphasis on position of the pieces, and absence of successful attempts to portray trees, people, houses,

* Adapted in part from *Degrees of Regression*, Lowenfeld, Margaret.

or like objects in a manner that utilizes both color and form realistically.

THE WECHSLER–BELLEVUE TEST

The monograph by Rapaport, Gill, and Schafer[51, 52] *Diagnostic Psychological Testing*, remains as the most thorough and authoritative report on the use of the Wechsler–Bellevue in the diagnosis of schizophrenia. In a later Menninger monograph, Schafer[55] continued the work of classifying various types of schizophrenic and neurotic disorders, giving descriptions of the expected psychological test signs he found to be associated with these conditions.

The value of the Wechsler–Bellevue, and the other Wechsler tests, in differential diagnosis has always been a matter of some controversy. Unfortunately, controversy has accompanied the use of every psychological diagnostic tool, both individually and as a group; thus, the Wechsler is no exception in this respect. The Wechsler is a valuable tool for differential diagnosis when it represents one of the several tests used as a battery. The Wechsler yields quantitative and qualitative signs.

Quantitative Wechsler Signs of Schizophrenia

1. Extreme variation in the sub-test scores, i.e. one sub-test has a score of seven or more points above or below another.

2. Relatively low comprehension, arithmetic, and picture completion scores.

3. Low similarity score occurring with high vocabulary score.

4. Verbal generally higher than performance.

5. Higher block design score than the average performance test scores. When overlapping clinical symptomatology raises doubt to the etiology of the condition, the relative score on the block design appears to be one of the most effective methods for differentiating between organic and functional psychoses. Schizophrenics usually have a block design score higher than their average performance score, and often above their average total test score. On the other hand, patients with organic brain disease tend to have scores on the block design sub-test which dip below their average performance score, and generally below their average total score on the Wechsler.

Qualitative Wechsler Signs of Schizophrenia

1. Failing easy test items and succeeding in relatively difficult ones in the same sub-test. This is true of all sub-tests.

2. Bringing in irrelevant materials, giving bizarre qualifications, or responding with inappropriate effect to any of the test questions.

3. Bland and thoughtless answers, especially on the information and vocabulary tests. This includes clang or sound associated answers such as, "spangle—to hit or spank", or personalizing and projecting such as, "fable—someone telling lies about you".

4. Schizophrenics frequently exhibit "aimed at but missed the target" responses in which the patient comes close to the answer, but, in the end, fails to arrive at it. Example: "table and chair are similar because they are both associated together, one fitting over and above the other—each contributing to make home what it should be".

The psychologist's task is complicated by the fact that the test signs associated with schizophrenia frequently overlap with signs characteristic of other pathologies. Few, if any, psychological test signs, can be called truly pathognomic. It is only by the judicious use of several diagnostic methods, carefully and painstakingly interpreted, and compared for common elements and consistent sign patterns, that he can arrive at a tentative conclusion. Test signs for schizophrenia will be characteristic, if the schizophrenic condition is obvious and unequivocal; but in that case there is less need for the use of psychological tests to arrive at a diagnosis. Psychological consultations are usually required when the patient's symptomatology raises doubts as to the primary diagnosis. The use of psychological tests are valuable when the psychological report resolves the doubts that would have required prolonged patient-observation. In other cases, the strength and nature of the psychological signs are useful in arriving at conclusions regarding prognosis, type of therapy to be used, and the etiological dynamics of the condition. The psychological test results may act as a base line to mark the progress of therapy, and to establish the recovery of the patient after treatment.

CHAPTER VII

ASSESSMENT OF NEUROSIS

The referring psychiatrist would like to know what is going on in the patient's mind that causes neurotic symptoms. In the evaluation of neurotics, the psychological report makes its major contribution by assessing the strength or weakness of the ego defenses, and by furnishing a description of the dynamic factors which are primarily responsible for the development of the neurosis.

Questionnaire type psychological tests are at a distinct disadvantage in the assessment of neuroses because the patient focuses his psychic effort in avoiding insights. It is improbable that paper-and-pencil type tests, which allow him to disguise his real feelings, will elicit dynamically meaningful materials. The Rorschach, the Thematic Apperception Test, and other projective type tests are ideally suited for this purpose. The tests to be described in this chapter are: the Rorschach, Thematic Apperception Test, the Kahn Test, Draw-A-Person Test, Sentence Completion Test, and the Word Association Test.

The Rorschach

There are a number of Rorschach signs designed to elicit the presence and strength of the ego defenses. Ego defenses are manifested on the Rorschach by negation and avoidance. The psychotic may respond immediately to a difficult card such as IX; whereas the neurotic may reveal the activity of his ego defenses by his hesitation to respond. The witch-like figures on this card are threatening to the neurotic, and the color organization is difficult for him. The neurotic does not respond as the psychotic by color naming, perseverating a previous concept, or giving a bizarre response. He shows his discomfort by uncertainty, increased vascular pressure, perspiration, and other physiological evidence of stress. The neurotic blocks when called on to respond to color. Color seems to stimulate his easily aroused anxiety.

The Psychoneurotic Indicators on the Rorschach

1. Rejection of one or more cards.
2. Few, if any, responses in which form and color are present with form dominating.
3. Increased reaction time, hesitation before responding, for those cards where shading is present.
4. "Color shock" manifested by discomfort at the presence of colors on the cards. Sometimes there is increased volubility, decrease in number of responses, increase in reaction time, expressed dislike or other comments on the color of the cards. This is also manifested by excessive turning of the color cards, and by physiological signs of increased stress.
5. Greater than average number of responses based solely on form of the blots, and ignoring shading, color, and other factors.
6. Over 50 percent of animal and anatomical responses.
7. Not over 25 responses.
8. Few, if any, human movement responses, with a relatively high number of animal responses.

Hysterical neuroses are differentiated from other types by the fact that color is prominent in these records, especially color responses in which form is a secondary consideration. In contrast with obsessive-compulsives, who offer a large number of responses, the records of hysterics are usually short. If a pure color response is given by the hysteric, it is often seen as "blood", and they are prone to describe the blots as either "weird", "horrid", or to exclaim, "how lovely! I like these colors". The obsessive-compulsive seldom gives a color dominant response. The latter is more apt to describe his own responses as "imperfect" and seems to be doubt-ridden. He attempts to be methodical, but often has difficulty in separating two adjacent areas appearing on the cards. The obsessive-compulsive is the only neurotic who, like the schizophrenic, uses contamination—such as "green worms seen to be coming out of the rabbit eyes", Card X. Some compulsives feel it is necessary to mention all parts of the blot, even when these are not used in concepts.

Persons with hypochondriasis, like compulsive patients, are likely to be over-attentive to details. On their records, one finds a plethora of anatomical responses, x-rays, and for reasons that are not entirely clear, one or more responses in which a "flower" or other botanical concepts are seen. Patients in anxiety states may show preoccupation with shading on the blots, focus on midline details, and exhibit an overawareness of symmetry. Depressed patients usually offer few responses, with prolonged reaction time. These patients are not apt to give whole card responses, and they seem particularly aware of the dark shading on the black-and-white cards. Self-depreciatory remarks concerning their responses reflect their impoverished self-confidence; slow reaction time corresponds with the general slowing up of physiological processes. In contrast, hypomanics may have many responses and their reaction time is fast. Whole card responses are common, but the quality of these responses is generally poor. A description of blot areas as "deteriorated, falling apart, or barely hanging on" is a projection of dysphoria, fear of disease, or aging processes. Where the depressed patient is preoccupied with the blackness of the cards, the hypomanic responds with excitement to the colors, ignoring the more subtle aspects, such as the intensity of the black-and-white shading, and texture. Extroverts, who react quickly to the environment, have more color than human movement responses. The reverse is true among introverts and persons who habitually use considerable self-control. Color responses, without presence of form, are suggestive of impulsive acting out of drives. The absence or dearth of color responses, sometimes indicates lack of capacity to utilize emotional outlets constructively.

Other characteristics of the neurotic personality are revealed on the Rorschach by the patient's use of the blot areas in making his concepts. A preponderance of whole cards responses is related to good intelligence, but an artificial and strained attempt to use wholes is a sign of status drive and a need for achievement. Preoccupation with small details on the card is seen most often among compulsive, depressed, or fault-finding individuals. Persons who are prone to use the white space are often oppositional. Diffused shading such as smoke or clouds, as well as a greater than average number of concepts seen as three-dimensional vista concepts, or mirrored reflections as implied by shading, are commonly associated with the presence of free floating anxiety. (That is, anxiety not channelized into areas where it can produce organic symptoms, or specific fears.) A prevalence of animal movement concepts is related to primitive instinctual drives and indicates immaturity when elicited on adult records. Too much awareness of texture on the cards seems to be related to hypersensitivity. Too little indicates a personality that is emotionally obtuse, lacking refinements, and low in capacity to establish rapport.

The emotional and intellectual counterparts of the Rorschach determinants are summarized.

Rorschach Determinants Related to Personality Characteristics

MOVEMENT—Psychic energy.

> Human—creative imagination, intelligence, capacity for interpersonal relationships and identification with others, inner fantasy life, and emotional maturity. Introversion is indicated when human movement responses significantly outweigh responses utilizing color.

> Animal—spontaneity, potential maturity, need for satisfaction of primitive instinctual drives.

SHADING—Deep inner feelings.

> Three-dimensional—self awareness, insight, introspection. As surface appearance and texture—"hairy", "fur", "rough", indicates sensitivity and tact. In the absence of form, excessive texture may imply lack of inhibitions and sensuality.

FORM—Intellectual control.

> Good form—contact with reality, stability, intelligence.
> Poor form—disorganized thoughts, lack of critical appraisal, distorted perception.

COLOR—Emotions.

> With form dominating—ability for appropriate affective response, adaptiveness, good emotional control.
> With form present, but color dominating—affective lability, seen in hysterical personalities, emotional instability, but also can be creativeness, or artistic temperament if some control factors are present in the record.
> Without any form—explosive, impulsive temperament, uncontrolled emotion, acting out potential.

H

Another method of assessment is to interpret the Rorschach responses symbolically. Concepts are related to a symbolic framework, producing results akin to free association. Some advocates of this method translate concepts, such as seeing bugs and spiders, as suggestive of "a rejecting, punitive, and destructive mother figure"; a calf or a puppy as reflecting a "role complementary to that of a patriarchal father figure; implying an immature and childlike orientation . . . associated with apathy, lack of striving, and a feeling of weakness".[49]

Proponents of the symbol method of Rorschach interpretation, offer hundreds of symbolic concepts and give possible personality correlates. Although this method is unsubstantiated by research, these symbolic Rorschach interpretations are useful in clinical practice. Each of the ten cards has its own concentration of symbols, and it is possible to obtain personality dynamics from the patient's differential reaction to the individual cards. The cards may be characterized as follows:

CARD I.   Initial reaction toward life; symbolic of earliest genetic experiences.

CARD II.   Elicits intensity and presence of uncontrolled, destructive impulses. Also gives first indication of color shock.

CARD III.   Capacity for interpersonal relations, identification with humans.

CARD IV.   Reaction toward authority and father figures.

CARD V.   The so-called "reality" card. The easiest card for forming the acceptable concept of a bird, bat, or butterfly.

CARD VI.   Sexual symbolization stimulus card. Reaction toward this card suggests attitudes towards sex.

CARD VII.   This is often thought of as the "mother image" card, and reflects feelings towards females, especially mother figures.

CARD VIII. Because of the good definition of the animals on either side of this blot, this is also a "reality card". However, it is in color, and therefore reality discernment must occur in the presence of emotional stimuli.

CARD IX. Stimulates phobic thoughts, and neurotics have difficulty responding to this card. This may differentiate them from psychotics. Because of the colors and threatening forms that they envision, some neurotics refuse to respond, saying that they "see nothing in it".

CARD X. This is thought of as the "frustration tolerance card". Some also regard reaction toward this card as an indication of capacity for social adaptation. The many individual blots on this card require that the test subject be able and willing to respond to stimuli of varying size, color, and dimension.

THEMATIC APPERCEPTION TEST (TAT)

The originators[44] of this thematic scheme of eliciting projections, evaluated the responses by a method sometimes referred to as the "Need-Press" method. Every sentence was analyzed to ascertain the hero's (main character of the story) needs in terms of the pressure, or "press" of the environment. Weighted scores were then assigned to these two factors, according to the types of needs and presses that were assigned to the central characters by the patient. Clinicians, however, found this method of evaluating the TAT cumbersome, and there followed a period of exploration by several authors for a way of scoring the test with less effort. Actually, many clinicians with experience do not formally score the test. However, they keep several scoring categories in mind, such as the adequacy of the hero, objects introduced and omitted, attribution of blame, signs of conflict, attitudes, types of inhibition, aggression, and the outcome of the dilemma or conflict situation in which the hero finds himself. The psychologist then draws generalized conclusions from these observations.

Neurotics reveal their own impulses, fears, ambitions, and aggressions by projecting them into the characters depicted in the drawings. The decision of whether these projected feelings are acceptable evidence of the presence of a neurosis is a subjective one. Therein lies the danger inherent in the interpretation. The diagnosis will depend not only on the perspicacity of the evaluator in recognizing neurotic projections, but also on the evaluator's own dynamics, which may be introjected. Thus, it is possible for him to erroneously interpret as neurotic projections what other psychologists might consider perfectly normal. It is safer to employ the TAT as a method of discovering thoughts which are preoccupying the patient, after the diagnosis of neurosis has already been established by other means. For example, Card 3GF shows a girl by an open door, hand over her face, in a position of emotional depression, and apparently crying. The test-subject who sees this situation as a girl "contemplating or thinking", and upon enquiry states that the girl probably is quite happy, may reveal that he characteristically uses the ego defense of denial and is not apt to admit subjective feelings of depresssion.

A test-subject may be projecting thoughts of suicide or death wishes, if he sees a person about to jump out of a window on Card 14. He may later depict the person in the drawing as no longer wishing to live and describe him as having lost hope and welcoming death. Several other cards lend themselves equally well to eliciting suicidal ideation. The evaluator will note carefully which of the pictures are rejected by the test-subjects; what kind of activities or situations seem to interest or disturb the patient; his attitude toward females, or his assignment of roles to the characters he describes. A relationship appears to exist between the outcome of conflicts, as envisioned by the test-subject, and the prognosis of therapy. On Card 12M showing the boy being hypnotized, the patient may predict a favorable outcome, or may decide that the results of the hypnosis are not going to be beneficial. By these reflections, the patient may be projecting his own motivation for improvement or recovery. It has been found that patients who consistently suggest an unfavorable outcome of TAT situations, have a guarded prognosis in terms of success of therapy.

A number of the TAT figures have a masked sexual identity, making it difficult, at first glance, to readily assign them a masculine or feminine role. The figure on Card 3BM, for example, could conceivably be called a boy or a girl. Insecurity, and conflicts regarding sexual identification, are mirrored in the perplexity and anxiety exhibited by certain patients when confronted by such figures. They express distress at being unable to decide whether the representation is male or female. They may have a similar dilemma in deciding whether the figures on Card III of the

Rorschach are male or female. Homosexual drives and latency problems lend themselves to projection by the test-subjects on a number of cards. The TAT is often used as an accompaniment of psychotherapy in order to determine whether there are concommitant role shifts, with improvement of function and reduction of symptoms.

Kahn Test of Symbol Arrangement

Indicators of Neurosis on the Kahn Test

Anxiety Reaction

1. Evidence of need for reassurance as manifested by anxious questioning, "How did I do?", "Did I do everything right?"
2. Self-deprecatory remarks, "I didn't do a good job", "I should have done it differently".
3. Excessive contact. Handling, turning and fingering the object, beyond curiosity.
4. Particular dislike of transparent objects, with remarks showing concern with their lack of substance and their transparency. Difficulty placing them over other objects (Arrangement II and III).
5. Difficulty in giving reasons for liking and especially disliking objects.
6. Lower estimate of recall ability than actual number of objects recalled.
7. Expressing concern at not knowing what "P" shape represents.
8. Changing objects after placing them. The more frequent the changes, the greater the anxiety.
9. Discrepancy between reason given for the arrangement and performance of the arrangement. Patient states "no reason" and the arrangement is obviously by color of objects.
10. High "B", "C", "E", or "F" scores depending upon how the test-subject handles his anxiety.

Obsessive-Compulsive Reaction

1. Systematically arranging objects on table before placing them on the strip; also may have difficulty in sorting and refuse to sort one or more objects.

2. Excessive meticulousness in naming objects. "A red small heart, smaller than the other ones, about one-quarter inch thick."
3. High "C" score. "C" among first three letters of symbol pattern.
4. Good recall scores.
5. Higher numerical element on symbol pattern than other types of neurotics.
6. Extremes in Contact—either excessive or none.
7. Excessive attempts to straighten objects—no slants or reversal of objects on the strip, unless slants are consistently the same in all arrangements.
8. Often an "E" score for first Reason for Arrangement and then "C" scores for the others. Design or balance emphasis in arrangement. May separate similarly shaped objects.
9. Reason for Liking or Disliking objects frequently is "well made" or "not well made", "good" or "poor workmanship".
10. Usually there is no variation in Direction of Arrangements; some start arrangement by placing objects at center of strip.

Hysterical Reaction

1. "F" present in letter element of symbol pattern.
2. "D" often prominent.
3. Seven to nine different letters in the letter element of the symbol pattern.
4. No objects placed in HATE, BAD, or DEAD.
5. Low recall (generally less than six objects correctly placed).
6. Evades or denies disliking objects.

In addition to the above signs, it has been found that the *depressed patient* is apt to have a slow arrangement time, place some object or objects in DEAD in sorting, and may resort to excessive straightening of objects on the strip. His symbolization may indicate subjective feelings of hopelessness, and he may place objects which he associates with himself in BAD or HATE. The *hypochondriacal* patient is apt to remark (heart shaped objects), "we need it to live", "health", "sickness". This type of patient may also place objects in DEAD in sorting, but not in HATE or BAD. *Dependency* is a component of certain types of character and behavior disorders. Some neurotics are also excessively dependent, and this is manifested by difficulty with the freedom of choice in making the arrangement. This type of patient may ask, "Arrange them any way at all?" seeking some help or guidance from the examiner. *Hypomanic patients* have fast reaction times, offer more than one reason for each arrangement, or tell "stories" connecting one object with another to explain their arrangements.

The KTSA symbol pattern yields an index of the condition and flexibility of the ego defenses. Lack of flexibility or weakness of ego defenses is indicated by having five or fewer letters in the symbol pattern. This usually implies acting out potential. Signs of the presence of active ego defenses are:

1. Slow reaction time.
2. Asking questions or seeking reassurance during test.
3. Changing objects after placing them.
4. Excessive contact or no contact.
5. Critical remarks regarding the test or test objects.
6. Color and form details in naming task.
7. Hesitations, vacillations in placing, symbolizing, and sorting objects.
8. Higher recall performance than estimated.
9. Difficulty (such as "no reason") in sorting objects according to Liking and Disliking (Arrangement IV), if concurrent with good reasons for arrangement of objects in Arrangements I, II, and V.
10. Six or more letters in the letter element of the symbol pattern, with an absence of any "A" scores.

In addition to the above, any of the previous signs of neurosis must be considered as a possible indication of active ego defenses.

MINNESOTA MULTIPHASIC PERSONALITY INVENTORY

The MMPI and other paper-and-pencil questionnaire type methods are preferred by some, because of the relative ease with which these tests can be administered and scored objectively. Additionally, statistical treatment of these tests is relatively easy, since they yield numerical scores. The objections are: The subject can fake some of the pencil-and paper tests, although the

MMPI has a built-in lie scale which is difficult to outwit. These tests depend entirely on verbal self-evaluation on the part of the patient, and may fail in tapping the deeper areas of the personality.

Needless to say, such tools should never be used as the sole psychometric contribution in any given situation. Their primary asset—and it is a very real asset—is to add objective support to the diagnostic impressions which have been arrived at subjectively. If the clinician feels that he may be emotionally involved in any given case, the additional use of objective tests such as the MMPI is necessary. The MMPI has been described as "a diagnostic instrument constructed entirely on the basis of clinical criteria".[29] The test is available in either card sorting or group booklet form. Since the patient must respond to more than 500 items, the card sorting task is less of a strain on the patient than the booklet form, which includes hundreds of items on each page. The patient's responses are scored and grouped according to ten diagnostic categories: Hypochondriasis, Depression, Hysteria, Psychopathic Deviate, Masculinity-Femininity, Paranoia, Psychathenia, Schizophrenia, Hypomania, and Social Introversion. In addition to the lie scale, the test also has a validity scale and a "K" scale, which is said to measure "defensiveness" in responding to the test questions. The patient's test scores are drawn on a psychograph and the presence of a condition is determined by the distance of the score from the norm. Hypochondriasis, Depression, and Hysteria are sometimes referred to as the "Neurotic Triad". When these three scores are raised, neurosis is implied. The presence of neurosis is also indicated when any single neurotic score is above the patient's mean.

DRAW-A-PERSON TEST (DAP)

Neurotic manifestations on the DAP include frequent erasures, shading, and reinforcement of lines. As we would expect, obsessive-compulsives show a tendency to overdo details. Thus, shoes may be shown with eyelets, laces, and bows; hands and arms with details including fingernails. These persons may pay particular attention to midline emphasis, details of pockets, neckties, and clothing in general. Often there is much erasing in an attempt by the patient to meet his own high standards of performance.

Hysterical patients are prone to produce empty looking drawings with eyes that are shown closed or which lack pupils. A prominent Adam's apple is sometimes seen in the drawings, and occasionally parts of the body are omitted. Omissions are most frequent among hysterics having conversion reactions. The drawings of patients suffering from neurotic depression are almost always small, projecting inferiority and low affect. The omission of arms in the drawings suggests withdrawal, or feelings of extreme helplessness on the part of the depressed patient.

OTHER TECHNIQUES

Utilizing the same general principles described in the above test, psychologists proceed with a large variety of materials in order to measure and evaluate neurotic behavior. The Make-A-Picture-Story (MAPS)[57] test utilizes a miniature theater and various types of cut-out cardboard figures which can be manipulated separately (description Chapter VIII). Although the MAPS is more cumbersome and complicated than the TAT, it permits the freer exercise of the imagination.

The House-Tree-Person (H-T-P)[13] technique is both qualitatively and quantitatively scored. In the appendix of the test manual, an analysis of chromatic drawings is offered.

Sentence completion and word association tests are widely used for eliciting neurotic thinking patterns, and for providing evidence of emotional blocking. This blocking is interpreted as indicating areas of guilt, anxiety, and repression. Among the areas most frequently tapped by word association and sentence completion techniques are:

AREA	STIMULUS PHRASE OR WORD
Interpersonal Relationships	People . . . What annoys me . . . Dancing . . . Most women . . .
Parental Relationships	My mother . . . My father . . . Back home . . . House . . .
Psychosexual Relationships and marriage	My wife . . . Marriage . . . Penis . . . Masturbation . . .
Self	I secretly . . . I wish . . . I . . . I hate . . . I need . . . I am best when . . . My greatest worry is . . . I can't . . . I regret . . .

AREA	STIMULUS PHRASE OR WORD
Past developmental History	In school . . . When I was a child . . . I failed . . . Back home . . .

Word association tests such as the one by Rapaport, Gill, and Schaffer[51, 52] use a wide variety of words and are so constructed that the "loaded" word—the one designed to stimulate a reaction —is placed near an innocuous word in order to catch the test-subject off guard, and to enable the examiner to observe difference in reaction. A few of the sixty words offered by Rapaport, Gill, and Schaffer are:

> book, father, paper, breast, curtains, trunk, doctor, dirt, cut, movies, cockroach, bite, frame, suicide, mountain, snake, house, vagina.

In summary, we may consider the neurotic person as one who tends to over-use the ego defenses, while normal persons use them in moderation. He is not satisfied with himself, but is so sensitive that he cannot realistically face the feeling of self-rejection. Instead, he hides these feelings from himself (except in certain types of neurosis, such as neurotic depression where the patient distorts by exaggerating his feelings of worthlessness). In the process of hiding them he develops a variety of symptoms. The use of psychological tests is indicated when there is doubt about the nature of the dynamics responsible for the symptom formation, and as a barometer for therapeutic potentialities.

CHAPTER VIII

EVALUATION AND TESTING OF CHILDREN

PARENTS, teachers, and juvenile authorities are becoming aware of the assistance the psychologist can render in the understanding of children. The problem child who causes disturbances in school, is frequently referred for psychological evaluation. Even more cogent is a thorough investigation of the "child with a problem", as distinguished from the problem child. The former may not exhibit any symptoms that draw the teacher's attention. His behavior may be exemplary, and of all the children in the class he may be the last to cause trouble. The lack of signs of outward disturbance is no guarantee of the absence of inner turbulence, and all experienced teachers realize that the child who behaves too well is in need of closer psychological scrutiny than the boisterous *enfant terrible*. There are many judges sitting in juvenile courts in certain sections of the United States who request psychological evaluation for youthful violators appearing before them. Judgment is not pronounced until the psychologist has reported his findings.

The successful child psychologist must be flexible, spontaneous, and able to show something of himself with which the child is willing to identify. Rigid adults, in whom the flicker of childhood has totally died out, and who represent to the child only the cold, steep, glacial promontories of authority, will fail in spite of forced smiles, kind words, and a profound knowledge of theory.

It is obvious from this, that not everyone otherwise qualified is temperamentally suited to examine children psychologically. We have found that interest in child psychology is not a sufficient criterion to guarantee success in testing children.

Persons who have children themselves are usually more understanding of the parental side of child problems than those who do not. Of course, there are exceptions, but psychologists who are parents themselves tend to refrain from showering all the blame for the child's misbehaving automatically on the father and mother. Two extremes must be avoided: casting parents invariably as villains in a drama in which the child is the ever defenseless, blameless victim of intolerable environmental circumstances—and viewing the child as a mere bundle of disturbing sights and sounds that can best be controlled by the use of the restrictive techniques of animal trainers. A child is an immature human being in the process of attempting to adjust to a perverse and complicated civilization by means of trial and error. Sympathy, sensitivity, a good awareness of reality, a sense of humor, and a genuine appreciation of the difficult task of parenthood, are qualities which the psychologist who wishes to work with children should possess.

Those who work psychologically with children, must also know how psychological instruments can be utilized with this type of population, and how the expected responses differ, not only between child and adult, but also among children of various age groups. A plausible case can be made for "blind analysis" of adult patient test responses. Here the sterile atmosphere of the laboratory is maintained and results are analyzed by a psychologist who is free from the contaminating influence of having seen or interviewed the patient personally. We have been quite successful with blind analysis in our own clinic. However, when children are involved, blind analysis can not be justified, since the observation of the child by the experienced clinician constitutes a most important factor in the assessment of the child's test responses. Psychometrists have been able to record such test concomitants as fear, hesitation, resistance, and these can be evaluated by the psychologist who integrates the test results into a final diagnostic impression.

There is no substitute for observation, and it begins the moment the child enters the room for the first time. Does he enter willingly or is he forced? Does he look around as he enters? Does he hesitate, or go directly to the chair which the psychologist offers? Does he look at the psychologist? Does he appear curious, frightened, or suspicious? Does he speak softly, slowly, rapidly, or distinctly? Does he choose his words carefully, or do they burst forth without restraint? Does the clothing he wears reflect care on the part of his parents? Is he too neatly dressed, implying an obsessive preoccupation with cleanliness and external appearance.

When he takes his chair, can he sit quietly or does he appear to be in constant motion? Does he exhibit any nervous mannerisms? Does he listen attentively? What is his approach to the test situation? How does he handle the materials?

Questions regarding a child's adjustment usually involve an evaluation of his intelligence. When a child's tested I.Q. clearly demonstrates that he is not utilizing his potential, the psychologist is confronted with the task of probing for possible explanations.

DRAWING TECHNIQUES

Almost every child likes to draw—even disturbed children. For this reason, art of one type or another usually has a place in the test battery designed for use with children. Age is no barrier in the use of drawing or painting techniques. Few children under two years of age are form conscious, and for this reason they will draw what they feel, instead of what they see. Maladjustment among very young children—two and a half years or less—is manifested by confinement to one color, when many colors are readily available. A child may become so involved with the task of drawing that he sticks to one color, and this case must be interpreted differently. Another consideration is the use of space. Normally, young children will use over half a page, making wide, roving strokes. The inhibited or anxious child will confine his work to narrow limits, using only a small portion of the paper. Such children may draw small circular objects in one of the corners. Others may make only a few dots, or one or two little lines. Hyperactive children of this age, range wildly over the paper, sometimes going beyond. Their movements are rapid and they finish the task quickly. They may dig deeply into the paper, tearing it with the pressure of their pencil, or crumble the crayon as they draw.

As children grow older, the form of the drawing plays an important part. The psychologist judges how well the child performed the task; how adequate the visual representation; how co-ordinated the psychomotor execution. Children may be asked to draw "whatever comes to your mind—draw anything you would like". The pertinency and maturity of the choice the child makes for the subject of his drawing is a valuable diagnostic aid. Subsequently the same child may be asked to draw his own family, and the psychologist will observe closely which family member is drawn first, or last; who will get the central spot, and who will be left out.   Such drawings help the psychologist evaluate the child's feelings about his parents and siblings, and understand the child's position in the family constellation. Judging the drawings requires experience, and because this is subjective, care must be taken in this evaluation.

THE RORSCHACH TEST AND EMOTIONAL GROWTH

The Rorschach is being increasingly used at both extremes of the human span of life.   This test has proven valuable in the evaluation of maturity and old age. Some psychologists have used it in a variety of gerontological studies. The use of the Rorschach with children is relatively new, but publications such as *Child Rorschach Responses—Developmental Trends from Two to Ten Years*, by members of the Gesell Institute of Child Development, [1] illustrate the increasing use of this technique with children of all ages.   This test is useful in establishing the emotional maturity level of a child, and ascertaining how it differs from the intellectual level as determined by intelligence tests. For example, we have recently seen a child in our clinic who was intellectually equipped to skip to the fifth grade. The Rorschach reinforced our observations that this child was barely at the third grade level in emotional development.   This inconsistency in mental and emotional maturity, prompted us to recommend that he be placed in the fourth grade rather than move to the fifth, as we believed the child would have difficulty making interpersonal contacts at school with children who greatly outstripped him in emotional development.

Psychologists working with children have found that Rorschach response patterns at the two-year level consist of the child's impressions, rather than an attempt at accurate discernment. Concepts such as "pretty flower" may be repeated several times as a response to color, regardless of the blot shape. At two and a half, the response is similar to that of the two-year old, except that there is more variety of content.   At three years, responses are less stereotyped, and of better form.   At four years, the average child gives fifteen responses. Human movement and animal movement responses have nearly doubled from the three-year level. At five years, the child shows high generalizing ability, and color responses are fewer than any succeeding age until ten. At five and a half, the equilibrium sometimes associated with five-year olds is breaking up, and this is manifested by an emphasis on small detail, and an increase in inanimate movement responses. Sometimes overt discomfort caused by the blots is expressed in initial exclamations.

Perception at six is increasingly accurate, and the form of the blots is used in about 80 percent of the responses. This trend continues until seven years, when a definite inwardizing of experience occurs, manifested by more movement and less color than at lower ages. At eight, the responses are much clearer, and the child expresses more uncertainty and qualifications. At nine, detail for the first time exceeds whole responses. At ten, the total weighted movement often outweighs the total weighted color responses.

An interesting study of Rorschach responses of adolescents was conducted at the Institute of Child Welfare, University of California,[40] and showed how developmental trends during the adolescent's growth are reflected on this test. Sex differences were noted in the study, and it was found that adolescent girls averaged a higher number of responses and, with striking consistency, made greater use of all the color variables.

The KTSA

Because it utilizes colorful materials, and the tasks are easily understood by children, the Kahn Test of Symbol Arrangement is being increasingly used in children's clinics and hospitals. In 1957, a paper presented to the American Psychological Association by Kahn and Fink, gave the results of a comparison of normal with emotionally disturbed children with the KTSA.[34] The investigators found that these groups could be distinguished by their symbol patterns. A ratio between the child's mental age and the numerical element of the symbol pattern, yielded an index of the extent of the disturbance. Further studies with children are required to determine to what extent this method will continue to substantiate the good results obtained thus far.

An earlier standardization of the test with children is reported in the Test Manual,[33] and shows developmental trends from ages 6 to 14 years. The average numerical element of the testee's symbol pattern rises gradually during these years, from an average low of 57 to a high of 92. The average numerical element on the symbol patterns of a small group of disturbed children remained at 58 regardless of their ages in the study described in the manual. "D" was the most common letter used by the disturbed children. This is in contrast with other letter elements elicited from the non-disturbed groups.

The manual also describes a method of determining the expected numerical element for different ages: the child's mental age, or chronological age [if mental age is not available] is multiplied by six. Thus, we would expect a 7-year old child to obtain a numerical element of 42, and a 10-year old child to obtain one of 60. If the child obtains lower score on the test, it is a sign in the direction of emotional disturbance. A score that is too high, one that far exceeds the expected, may suggest the use of protective coloration by the child. He may utilize the culture as a means of appearing brighter and more sophisticated than he actually is. This pseudo-sophistication has often led parents and teachers to assume that the intelligence test was wrong. Such children make such an excellent impression on adults that their lack of real capacity is obscured.

Perhaps the main value of the KTSA lies in the chance it affords the examiner to watch the child at work. The repetitive nature of the tasks gives the examiner an opportunity to see whether the child approaches a new situation with initial enthusiasm, and then rapidly loses interest; or whether he maintains good performance throughout. Improvement in performance of the tasks as the child proceeds is related to good prognosis to therapy and general adjustment. Even though the child fails to give reasons for his first and second arrangements, there is still grounds for favorable prognosis, if he demonstrates orderliness, and good organization in the final arrangement of objects on the strip. The child's estimate of his ability to replace the objects exactly as he had them before; the associations in the sorting task, and the amount of slanting and disorderliness in placing the objects on the strip, all play a role in the final evaluation. They measure how well the child utilizes symbols in reaching out to his environment for the cultural support that society offers him as a framework for his emotional growth and mature development.

APPERCEPTION TESTS

Children who inhibit most severely are often the ones who project most readily. Apperception tests, which give the child a chance to tell a story, offer an effective method for eliciting information regarding the nature of the child's conflicts and insecurities. Murray's Thematic Apperception Test[44] was designed primarily for adults and older adolescents, but is used in child guidance clinics because some children over 7 years of age are insulted at being shown pictures of animals in human stances or in ludicrous positions. Other psychologists feel that children can best identify with animals and, therefore, justify the use of pictures such as those in the Children's Apperception Test, which was designed for use with children from 3 to 10 years of age.[8]

Another test using cartoon pictures of dogs exclusively,[12] emphasizes the developmental focal points following psychoanalytic theory. The pictures are designed to elicit feelings of rejection, and to reveal the presence of conflicts in such areas as sibling rivalry, mastery, aggression, masturbation, oral gratification, and toilet training.

The list of new apperception tests designed for use with children is growing constantly. The Michigan Picture Test[28] was designed for use with children from 8 to 14 years of age, and consists of sixteen pictures; four to be used with boys, four with girls, and eight with boys and girls. The plates contain figures of children, and are structured to elicit reactions towards home and school, as well as conflicts regarding adolescence, parents, peers, and sexual drives.

The Symond's Picture-Story Test,[59] designed for use with teenage children 12 to 18 years old, depicts young adults in situations which Symonds believes effectively elicits clues regarding the manner in which the test-subject handles hostility, eroticism, moral standards, status drives, guilt, depression, and sublimation.

One of the most effective apperception tests was developed by Shneidman in 1952,[57, 58] and permits the test-subject to structure

I

his own thema. Because the test permits manipulation and selection of background, dynamics may be revealed when the test-
subject refuses to project significant material verbally, or blocks
verbally. The Shneidman technique consists of sixty-seven cardboard figures, animal and human. There are twenty-two scenes
representing large variety of backgrounds for use with the slotted
stage which holds the materials the test-subject selects. The
method enables the subject to create a psycho-drama, in which
he plays all the roles. The figures include male and female adults,
children, persons of various racial groups, legendary and fictitious
characters, as well as silhouettes and figures with blank faces. The
background scenes include a schoolroom, nursery, living-room,
bathroom, attic, cellar, bedroom, shanty house, bridge, raft, street,
cemetry, forest, cave, doorway, landscapes, and scenes from story
books. The test instructions require the subject to tell a story
about the situation he has created, explain the scene, the selection
of characters, and give the outcome of the story. Insight is gained
into the subject's emotional difficulties, and his efforts to handle
these. The fact that this technique requires the test-subject to play
several roles, permits verbalizations which serve to reduce tensions,
and therefore acts as a therapeutic as well as diagnostic tool.

Other techniques which permit the child to play and act out a
variety of needs, and to display his creative imaginations, utilize
small life-like objects such as animals, people, houses, trees, which
the child is permitted to handle freely, and to use in building a
world as he conceives it. Several varieties of toy world building
techniques are available. The World Test designed by Buhler
and Kelly,[14] presents realistic miniature reproductions of a
variety of things seen by children and encourages them to play
with these toys in any way they desire. In scoring the test, the
examiner notes the type of people, animals, or objects used in the
play, and analyzes the activity with the aid of a scoring sheet which
describes signs of aggressive, empty, or distorted worlds. The
Lowenfeld Mosaic Test[38] enables the child to use colors and
shapes spontaneously, and has some of the advantages of free-
association drawings. Plate 4 illustrates the performance of a
6-year old child using this method.

The play methods designed for testing the child in the psychologist's office represent a compromise between no play

opportunity, and the ideal situation of unhampered play with real toys in a room designed for this purpose. Practically all modern, well-equipped child guidance clinics have one or more rooms in which the psychologist may observe the child's activities through a one-way viewing screen. These rooms are usually stocked with a variety of toys, including large-sized play-horses upon which a child can climb, building blocks, tools, drawing materials, stuffed animals, and puppets. Some rooms are prepared for special situations, and the toys are then carefully selected to enable the child to project specific needs or anxieties which the psychologist and his staff wish to study. Thus a child may find female puppets in the room, or only dolls and baby clothes. In the selection of toys and equipment, the age and sex of the child is taken into account, in addition to the specific diagnostic and therapeutic problems involved in the case. If the child is a member of a play group, sociometric techniques developed by Moreno and others[43] may be used. This method measures attraction and repulsion between individuals in a group, and permits the data to be drawn graphically in the form of sociograms, which can be examined and studied at leisure. A knowledge of the sociometric status of a child adds another dimension from which personality of the child may be viewed. Additionally, reports of the child's behavior in the classroom, his academic progress, description of his home adjustment, relationships with other children, his physical health, and the pattern of his growth, are all portions of the total fabric which must be studied in its entirety.

Since children are apt to be changeable and unpredictable, the psychologist can obtain a clearer picture if he sees the child several times and under varying circumstances. For this reason, it is also desirable that testing not be completed on a single day. Both parents should be interviewed, if possible, and a case history of their own adjustment should be provided by the social worker.

The authors have developed questions, which may be used in part with children in the 5 to 9 years age group to help discover conflict areas which may have been overlooked.

These questions are:

1. Imagine that you are a magician and could make any changes in the world that you wanted, tell me whom you would change and how you would change the world.

2. Suppose you could turn people into animals, tell me what people you would turn into animals, and what kind of animals they would be?

3. Name some things that are right to do, things that good people do?

4. Name some things that are wrong to do, things that bad people do?

5. What are you going to be when you grow up?

6. If you were the richest person in the world, name some of the things that you would do with your money? Tell me some of the things you would buy?

7. What kind of things make you feel angry? Happy? Sad?

8. If you had a whole day to do what you wanted, name some of the things you would do?

9. Name some of the things you would like to get for Christmas, or for your birthday?

10. Who do you like best in your family? Mother? Father? Sister? Brother?

11. Are you mostly happy? Unhappy?

12. Tell me some things that make you feel afraid? What things scare you? What are you afraid of?

13. Do you think that children in other families are luckier than you? If so, why are they luckier?

14. Could you give me your own idea of why your parents took you to see me?

15. Tell me, what is the best thing that ever happened to you? What is the worst thing that ever happened to you?

16. Do you have any secrets that you wouldn't tell anyone? Do you worry about these secret thoughts?

17. What kind of games do you like to play? Would you rather play alone, or play with other children?

18. With what kind of children do you like to play most? Boys or girls? Children who are older than you? Children who are younger than you? Children who are your own age? Children who play rough sports, or children who play quiet games?

19. If you were shipwrecked on a desert island, and could only have one other person with you—whom would you choose? If you could have two persons, three persons, four persons, etc., who would you choose?

20. I am a psychologist and my job is to help people by trying to understand how they feel. Most of us have some problems and worries, and that is true of a grown-up like myself as well as of children. I know that you don't really know me very well yet, but let me be your friend. Is there anything you wish to talk about before we begin?

Questions such as these supplement, but cannot replace, a thorough and objective description of the environmental pressures and conditions which the child faces. We cannot expect an evaluation based on routinely selected psychological tests to be accurate. The psychologist must be aware of the child's social background and his socio-economic level in order to utilize his interview techniques to full advantage. A knowledge of the child's home life is a prerequisite in determining which test materials, or test methods are most likely to be successful. A knowledge of the school adjustment helps the psychologist prepare for testing the child's intelligence.

Many times, in the course of his evaluation of children, the psychologist will be thrown upon his own resources, and will have to create his own methods of best reaching the child with whom he is working. He may have to joke with the child to see how he reacts toward the attempt to be funny. He may have to feign ignorance of a simple question to see whether the child helps him answer, and to note what the child's reaction is towards an adult who does not appear to know simple answers. In all these probings, and in the clowning, care must be taken that the child does not lose respect, but considers the visit seriously.

To be both a fool and a wise man, to represent authority and still be permissive, to be an adult, and yet have retained enough of childhood for the child to feel identification and rapport, requires a versatility and flexibility which is rare. The requirement of a thorough knowledge of testing techniques, and a good understanding of the emotional and physical growth of children, are required for success in the field of child psychology. The use of well selected psychological instruments, correctly applied and carefully interpreted, are of considerable help in the difficult and highly responsible job that falls upon the adult who attempts to understand the function and the future of a child.

CHAPTER IX

PSYCHOLOGICAL TESTS IN VOCATIONAL AND EDUCATIONAL GUIDANCE

We all know that psychological tests are applied to a great variety of situations, and their use for clinical and diagnostic purposes represents only one area of their general use—an area with which this book is principally concerned. The same persons who may wish to know how the psychologist obtains his clinical impression, may have a valid interest in the related area of vocational guidance and rehabilitation. How does the vocational counselor arrive at his conclusions regarding his client's job fitness, or his vocational aptitude? Many hospitals, especially mental institutions and treatment centers for physically handicapped, employ vocational counselors to assist the patient return to the important, face-saving task of making a living. To be a self-supporting, contributing member of society is an important factor in the total psychological rehabilitation of a patient discharged from a hospital. The importance of sound vocational guidance is a matter in which physicians, as well as other persons on the treatment team, have a legitimate interest.

There are six primary considerations in vocational guidance. These are: (1) interest, (2) aptitude, (3) personality, (4) training opportunities, (5) availability of funds and time for training, and (6) employment opportunities.

Good vocational guidance cannot take place if any one of the six factors we have mentioned does not relate harmoniously with the others. If a young man is interested in becoming a veterinarian, has the aptitude and personality, sufficient money, and has found employment opportunities, the problem of the availability of training remains. At one time there were very few schools of veterinarian medicine in certain areas of the United States, and there are some countries where there are no schools of this kind. In other fields, training opportunities may be so limited that a young person planning his future may wish to explore other occupational opportunities than the one which represents his first choice. A girl may have everything required for the occupation of stenographer, including high interest, superior aptitude for typing, clerical work, and handling of correspondence, plenty of opportunity for training, as well as employment opportunity. However, if she lacks the personal qualities required to get along with other office workers and with the employer, all six requirements are not in harmony.

The six necessary qualities may be visualized as a train. Interest is the engine which pulls the other cars. Aptitude is the coal car which follows on the heels of interest, giving it the energy to become dynamic and move forward. The passenger cars of personality, training opportunity, funds for training, and employment opportunity follow in this order. At the end of the preparation period, when the question of earning a living becomes the foremost consideration, the engine is reversed so that it can push employment opportunity. Two cars, training opportunity and funds for training, having safely arrived at their destination, are shunted from the rest of the train. In their place a new car is added—advancement opportunity. Now the train moves on over the hills and valleys of career satisfactions, toward its final destination, retirement and pension. Whether the trip will be smooth or rough, long or short, depends on the type of terrain that must be traversed, the serviceability of the equipment, availability of the power supply, and the number of stops required. We have endeavored to supply the reader with a time-table to help him decide whether any particular train will be on schedule. It is called a Summary of Vocational Guidance Factors.

Let us consider the six areas of vocational guidance in some detail. Interest is usually one of the first considerations when selecting a vocation. In view of the increasing number of vocational specialities, young people often feel at a complete loss in relating their interests to a meaningful occupation. Persons wishing to explore their interests find clarification from a simple cataloging of their interests on a yes-no basis. Even without any clear idea of present vocational interests, students readily answer:

Do you like to work with people?

Do you like to help people who are in trouble?

TABLE 11. SUMMARY

FACTORS			SIX AREAS
	I INTERESTS	II APTITUDES	III PERSONALITY
A ORIGIN	1. Acquired by identification or observation. 2. Results of inborn skills. 3. Because of earning potential.	1. Inborn traits and skills.	1. Constitutional fa tors and enviro mental conditio ing.
B HOW TO IDENTIFY OR REVEAL THE PRESENCE OF AREAS	1. Interest tests. 2. Hobbies. 3. Favorite school subjects. 4. Tasks liked in past work experience.	1. Intelligence tests. 2. Aptitude tests. 3. School grades. 4. Past work performance.	1. Personality tests. 2. Case history. 3. Interview. 4. Reports fro teachers or pa employers.
C DISQUALIFYING ELEMENTS NEGATING POSITIVE FINDINGS	1. Evidence that interests are pseudo-interests or transient.	1. Insufficient health or strength for tasks. 2. Personal appearance, size, weight.	1. Neurosis. 2. Psychosis. 3. Emotional imm turity.
D FACTORS AFFECTING VOCATIONAL PREDICTIONS	1. Change of interests with time or experience. 2. Changes in salary or earning potential.	1. Incorrect assessment of aptitudes. 2. Maturation of new aptitudes. 3. Health changes.	1. Incorrect asses ment of personalit 2. Changes due situational stress disease. 3. Maturation or e vironmental facto not anticipated.

VOCATIONAL GUIDANCE FACTORS

CONSIDERATION			FACTORS
IV TRAINING OPPORTUNITIES	V FUNDS AND TIME AVAILABILITY	VI EMPLOYMENT OPPORTUNITY	
1. On the job apprenticeship. 2. School or university.	1. Parents. 2. Self-employment. 3. Stipends and scholarships.	1. Government service. 2. Private economy. 3. Self-employment.	A ORIGIN
1. School catalogs. 2. Newspaper advertisements. 3. Union or government information agencies.	1. Analysis of the sources of funds for studying.	1. Union or government informational services. 2. Personal contacts. 3. Survey of economic conditions.	B HOW TO IDENTIFY OR REVEAL THE PRESENCE OF AREAS
1. Absence of, or distance to training facilities.	1. Obligation to support family or self.	1. Racial or religious discrimination affecting applicant. 2. Age, too young or too old for the job.	C DISQUALIFYING ELEMENTS NEGATING POSITIVE FINDINGS
1. New schools or training facilities. 2. Closing of schools or training facilities. 3. Changes in admission requirements. 4. Changes in training requirements.	1. Death or illness of person supplying support. 2. Loss of scholarship. 3. Loss of funds for other reasons.	1. New industries, inventions or processing methods, automation. 2. Movement of industries or population shifts. 3. Major disasters, including wars, or preparation for wars. 4. Revolutions in government or political upheavals. 5. Depressions, recessions, or inflationary periods. 6. Labor, management, conditions, strikes, or restrictive practices, legislation, licensing, new laws of certification.	D FACTORS AFFECTING VOCATIONAL PREDICTIONS

Would you prefer to work with tools, rather than manage an office?

Do you prefer participation in outdoor sports to reading a book or writing a story?

Questions of this type are used in what are called interest inventories. The scoring of these inventories brings together interest clusters, which have a meaningful relationship to vocational areas. These areas usually include: arts, interpersonal relationships, science, engineering, sales and persuasive interests, agricultural, clerical, social service, and mechanical interests. In addition, some tests indicate the socio-economic level of interests. Thus, there are different score patterns for auto mechanics and graduate mechanical engineers, although both of these occupations require high mechanical interest.

Many persons do not respond well to true and false, or multiple choice questionnaires. However, these tests can be used with groups—a time-saving device. When there is time for individual attention, several new devices are available. One of these is known as the Vocational Apperception Test (VAT), by R. B. Ammons,[3] and consists of a set of eighteen drawings printed on cards, of persons working in various vocational tasks with typical surroundings. Ten of the cards were designed for women and eight for men. The pictures include representations of teachers, officer workers, physicians, engineers, lawyers, salesmen, dieticians, social workers, laboratory technicians, and others. The originators of this test state that it has the advantages of a projective technique, in that free association with the cards may elicit tension areas and show the inter-relationship of tensions and interests.

A technique constructed by Kahn,* while employed as a senior vocational counselor for the University of California, consisted of cards covering ten different vocational interest areas. Photographs portraying typical vocational activities were glued on these cards so that low socio-economic levels of the occupation were shown at one corner. The higher socio-economic levels associated with occupational tasks of increasing difficulty were placed at the opposite corner. Additionally, photographs illustrating concrete and abstract areas of every vocational category were separated and shown on separate corners of the card.

*Unpublished Technique.

Thus, the card on medicine showed routine tasks in ascending order of difficulty—changing bedpans, making beds, washing laboratory equipment, taking blood samples, working with a microscope, and taking x-rays. Laboratory work, in which there is no contact with the patients, was shown in a different section of the card from tasks in which a patient relationship was involved. Photographs of work in radiology, pathology, and bacteriology were on one corner and psychiatry and the non-laboratory occupations in the opposite corners. Nursing activities were portrayed near the center of the card. Another section showed people at work with medical statistics, or medical illustrations. The testee was given the opportunity to select the card he preferred, and asked to point to the sections on the cards that appealed to him most. An eleventh card was used, which showed pictures of all the vocations and different levels arranged in random order, to be used as a validity check on the subject's earlier choices. Sufficient variation of location was introduced so that one could be relatively sure that those who consistently selected high, low, or middle ranges for preferred job levels, had ambitions which corresponded to these levels.

Interest tests and devices such as we have described are only one of many different methods that help the vocational counselor in determining interest areas. Hobbies, avocational interests, preferred reading material, as well as school subjects, offer important clues useful to the counselor. Field trips or excursions to factories, shops, offices, laboratories, which give opportunity for personal observation of people at work in various occupations, should not be overlooked as sources for establishing interests. The counselor must check all the reasons for job preference given by an individual to determine if he is dealing with real or spurious interests. Spurious interest, or pseudo-interests are those which are based only on financial gain, the role of respectability, or the power which a particular job offers. If a person would "like to like" an area of vocational activity, rather than actually liking it, he has pseudo-interests in this occupation. A favorite uncle may be a lawyer, and because he admires him, his nephew may think he would like to become a lawyer too. Actually, he may have low verbal interests, does not like speaking in public, and not care for any of the elements that go into the making of a law career. Law interest is, for the boy, only a way of showing his love for his uncle. This pseudo-interest in law can plunge him into an unsuitable career.

Aptitude

Many people are confused by the word aptitude. They think of ability, intelligence, and sometimes even of interest, as aptitudes. Aptitude means potential capacity to learn or perform. We emphasize the word, potential, because the crux of aptitude is that it denotes an ability which is not yet manifested. A person may have a high musical aptitude without ever having played a note. High musical aptitude means that if a person were trained in music, he would learn quickly, and after the training he would perform well. Only after training is successfully completed, does a person have *ability* in music. Ability is what he can do; aptitude is his potential to do this. Ability is an aptitude which has had a favorable environment in which to mature. Vocational counselors guiding students are not particularly interested in ability, except as an indication of interests and aptitudes. A youngster may have gained ability in working some of the equipment in his father's machine shop, but his predominant aptitude may be in an area far removed from machinery of any type.

Counselors use large varieties of aptitude tests designed to elicit inborn skills and native capacities. Tapping an inborn skill is no easy task, and the methods available for this purpose require constant re-evaluation. Aptitude tests deal primarily with factors such as finger dexterity, visual acuity, and other basic capacities required in various occupations. Intelligence tests are aptitude tests, because they attempt to measure capacity. This capacity may or may not be reflected in terms of school achievement, or in ability to perform a job. Knowing aptitude levels, gives a prediction of trainability along specific vocational lines. Aptitude plays an important role when retaining must take place in rehabilitation after bodily injury, or when health does not permit continuation of work in the field in which a person was trained. For young people who have not had the opportunity to learn their capabilities from life experiences, there exists an array of aptitude tests which vary greatly in regard to proven worth. Such tests cover the field of teaching, nursing, medicine, engineering, law, art, music, journalism, and salesmanship, just to mention a few. As the competition for careers becomes keener, the weeding-out processes, by necessity, become more mechanical and impersonal. Tests have the advantage of being objective and rapid. They yield scores which permit analysis of tested traits, and comparison of any one person's performance with that of previously tested groups. When group tests are given, cataloguing and filing of test information for future reference is possible so that modifications in the test content can be made if necessary. The arbitrary use of tests as the chief instruments in decisions that vitally affect the testee's future is not recommended. No robot, no matter how ingenious, can replace the human judgment of a trained and experienced observer.

At the present stage of their development, the use of psychological aptitude tests in forming career decisions seems justified, when they are used as guides that indicate direction, but not when taken as oracles that predict destination. Aptitude test results must never be considered without taking the testee's vocational interests into account. Potential skill will not have much vocational significance if the subject lacks interest in the career field to which his aptitudes point. The vocational counselor often has to do a considerable amount of juggling between interests, aptitudes and employment opportunities, before he can consider the all-important question of what training to recommend.

Personality

Most people get discharged from jobs because of personality failure, rather than from inability to perform the work. Of all the qualities we have described, personality is the most difficult to test and evaluate. Publishers of the paper-and-pencil personality tests admit difficulty in designing instruments in which the testee cannot manipulate. This is only one of the shortcomings of such tests, and not the most important one. Personality is an elusive, tenuous, and many-faceted concept that does not lend itself to analysis by multiple-choice type questions. The use of paper-and-pencil tests may be justified for screening large groups of applicants; however, there is no substitute for individually administered projective techniques. These require more time to administer and to evaluate, but they are correspondingly more efficient in eliciting multi-dimensional personality characteristics.

TRAINING OPPORTUNITIES

The competition in training for higher level jobs will become keener with the increase of automation, and the corresponding decrease in need for non-skilled and semi-skilled workers. This will place an added strain on training facilities. Expansion of the means for acquiring learning seldom keeps pace with the demand for increased education. Therefore, as time goes on, the question of how to obtain training in the field in which an individual has demonstrated interest and aptitude may become more difficult to answer. In the United States, in certain fields such as medicine, applicants for training roam far from home and often conduct extensive campaigns in order to secure acceptance. There are also new vocations for which training programs are not yet available. This situation exists in countries which are in a stage of new development calling for skills and knowledge which cannot be imparted by institutions of learning in the country itself. Students in such a country must take part or all of their training in other countries where adequate training facilities exist. Who can afford the time and money that such travel and training may require? These are questions with which the vocational counselor must deal realistically. If scholarships are available, he must ascertain the individual's eligibility for these. A candidate may have demonstrated exceptionally high interest, aptitude, and the proper personality for a given profession, but if he lacks the means required to obtain the training, a reappraisal of his vocational objective may be necessary. This is particularly true for the applicant with family obligations, debts, or when ill health makes it difficult for him to earn extra money. Persons have obtained training in spite of what appeared to be insurmountable obstacles. These exceptions show that the human spirit can triumph over almost any odds if sufficiently motivated. Whether or not he considers the obstacles in his way as insurmountable, the applicant should weigh the factors of training opportunity and means of support, as realistically as he must face the limitations of his capacity and direction of his interests.

Employment Opportunities

Employment represents the final goal of vocational guidance. It is tragic that vocational counselors sometimes lose sight of goals in their preoccupation with requirements and procedures. Common errors involve considering employment opportunities as static. They study the findings of national or private surveys on industrial expansions, and resulting employment opportunities, but fail to realize predictions may be wrong because of factors not considered when predictions were made. In 1946 and 1947, word reached most vocational counseling centers in the United States that opportunities for employment of engineers were limited. Young men were dissuaded by vocational counselors from training for engineering professions at that time, because of the information supplied by these surveys. The advent of the cold war and increased military preparation, together with the invention of new processes, unexpected demand for consumers goods, reversed the employment trend a few years later. An unprecedented number of engineers were then required, and there was much competitive bidding for their services. Some of the unanticipated shortage of engineers could have been prevented if vocational guidance counselors had interpreted the 1946–47 reports on future employment needs more cautiously.

The summary of vocational guidance factors, Table 11, presents six general factors affecting vocational prediction of employment opportunities. In addition to these, there are specific limitations which apply more to one country or type of employment than to others. These include racial and religious prejudice, personal connections with employment resources, and politics. No one can say in advance how prominent a role any of the limitations will play in a given case. A "good" man may get ahead regardless of the obstacles that are in his path. However, a good man will realistically appraise the forces arrayed against him, and take them into proper account when making decisions.

The Counseling Responsibility

The responsibilities of vocational counseling are not always taken seriously. Some school administrators insist that every child must be counseled without realizing that poor counseling, based on insufficient data, is worse than none. There are schools where a teacher, relatively untrained in counseling methods, is given the title of "counselor" and assigned to help students make far-reaching educational and vocational decisions. In some cases, students select occupations designated by the counselor who devoted only a few minutes to the perusal of the student's personality test, interest inventory scores, and school grades. Some school authorities take pride in the fact that students in their school are given guidance, even though the methods of guidance are questionable and superficial. Real harm can be done by mass-produced guidance programs, even if those who work in these programs are technically trained to acceptable levels of competence. The best trained and most conscientious counselor may become a victim of mechanization if he finds himself faced with the alternative of resigning from his job, or yielding to the pressure of his superiors. On the basis of several years of personal experience in the field of vocational guidance, we suggest the following principles:

1. No person should be forced to seek vocational guidance. Students should apply for vocational counseling on their own initiative, at the advice of their teachers, or parents, without coercion.

2. Vocational counselors must be qualified psychologists who are able to detect the presence of emotional disturbance if it is masked as vocational dissatisfaction or as an educational problem.

3. Facilities for referring students to mental health clinics must be available, and students must be referred to these clinics when emotional problems are recognized as underlying vocational or educational problems.

4. A counselor must never be assigned a definite number of counselees to be processed within a given time. Sufficient time must be provided so that he can do a thorough job in each case. The matter of how much time is required with each counselee must be left to the counselor's own judgment.

5. The counselor must use only sound psychological tests and techniques, and must use enough of them to avoid reaching conclusions on insufficient evidence. If a question of personality difficulty arises, he must know how to use or obtain the use of

projective techniques. The counselor must never be required to use tests in which he has no confidence, or in which he lacks experience.

6. The counselor must be aware of the limitations of vocational guidance, and must respect the inherent right of every person to make his own plans regarding his future. Instead of telling the counselee what to do, he should present the facts, explain their significance, mention their limitations, and then permit the counselee to make his own decisions.

7. The counselor should have at his disposal library facilities, and other sources of information to which the counselee may be referred. He should maintain contacts with persons in various professions so that he may keep abreast of new developments having a bearing on employment conditions and opportunities. Time should be alloted the counselor for keeping up to date with the current literature on guidance and techniques of counseling.

8. The counselor must not be required to follow a mechanical format in reporting the findings, nor should he be asked to report on matters not related to the counseling situation. He should not make statements which he cannot support with evidence. The length and content of the report should be left to the judgment of the counselor.

The desire to fit each man to a proper niche in a nation's economy is a natural accompaniment of increasing industrialization and specialization. The means of insuring the "right job for the right man" represents a challenge that we are far from meeting. Experience has shown that poor counseling is much worse than none. Every person has the right to decide his own vocational future, and to embark on a career which does not follow the counselor's recommendations. Mass counseling programs for schools or universities are deplored, unless individual testing is employed, and a sufficient number of trained counselors are available to give each student as much attention as required. Emphasis on counseling should not be on a student's future vocational possibilities *per se*. Instead, the evaluation should be focused on the student himself, as a human being, with his vocational possibilities as only one aspect of the total picture.

K

CHAPTER X

REPORTING THE PSYCHOLOGICAL FINDINGS

THE impressions gained from the performance of patients on the psychological tests must be reported in intelligible and meaningful language. The report must be clear and concise. The terminology and technical wordage used must be in keeping with the abilities of the referring agents to understand them. Certainly, highly technical reports, full of medical terms, sent to a non-medical agency are meaningless. Judicious care and tact are essential in informing individuals of the findings and conclusions reached from the tests. In some agencies this task is delegated to the psychologist. In discussing the findings with parents, care must be taken not to provoke unnecessary anxiety. Yet significant and essential findings must not be withheld. The total effort of the evaluation culminates in the writing of the report. The level of communication marks the psychologist, either as an incompetent person or a specialist who interprets his findings cautiously, with confidence in his art.

We have selected three cases and adapted them for use as illustrations. Names and background material have been changed to insure that the principals involved will not be recognized. These reports are not presented as typical of what is found in all psychological practice. They were selected specifically to complement the content materials of this book, and to offer a sample of reporting results.

CASE 1

Referral Information

James, a 13-year old, was referred to the psychologist by the social worker of a municipal guidance center. An evaluation was requested to assist her in counseling the mother and child. A visit to the center had been recommended by the boy's teacher.

James was described as a behavior problem in school. He displayed little interest in his school work, was continuously clowning, and on occasion, had severely beaten younger children. He was not amenable to correction and resented discipline. The mother told the social worker that she could not understand this child. She emphasized she had done "the best I could" in raising him, but he never responded to her love or affection. James has one younger brother. Both parents say they wish James were more like him.

Interview Impression

The mother, a serious, unsmiling woman, who appeared older than her 35 years, started the interview with, "My family life is a happy one, but James does not enter into the spirit of this happiness." After this she talked in a dull listless voice, describing James' shortcomings and contrasting them to the virtues of the younger boy. The mother appeared to be critical of James and hostile toward the examiner.

After the mother left, James reluctantly entered the office. He was a thin, delicately built boy, somewhat smaller than the average 13-year old. He was dressed in clean blue jeans and a white T-shirt. His shoes were worn and his hair was meticulously combed but in need of cutting. From his expression he appeared to be a serious, unhappy, and hostile child. During the testing he became more friendly, especially after being praised and encouraged.

Tests Administered

1. The Stanford Binet, Revised, Form L.
2. The Rorschach Test of Personality Diagnosis.
3. The Draw-A-Person Test.
4. The Kahn Test of Symbol Arrangement.

Test Findings

James passed all the tasks on the Stanford–Binet Test at the 12-year level. At the 13-year level, he passed all but the "Memory for Words". As he attempted to repeat the words given by the examiner, he started to stutter. On the second series he flushed, and said angrily, "I can't do that". He was persuaded to try again and failed after three words. It is possible that anxiety may have been a factor in his inability on this task. On the 14-year level, he failed the vocabulary, ingenuity, and abstract words sub-tests. At the 15-year level, James failed all the tasks. He attained a mental age of 13 years and 4 months on the Binet. Since James was 13 years and 1 month of age, his I.Q. was 102.

It was found that the average I.Q. of the children who attended James' school corresponded with the national norms. Therefore testing ruled out the possibility that James' behavior problem stemmed from a lack of native intelligence.

James reacted to the initial Rorschach card with the question, "Is this supposed to be something I can recognize?" He responded to the rest of the cards with popular and easily perceived concepts but failed to see any humans, except "two clowns" on Card II. The reaction to the first card suggested insecurity and, possibly, hostility toward the test situation. Lack of ability to see human beings on Cards III and VII is characteristic of adolescents who have difficulty in interpersonal relationships. His only humans were "clowns". This concept is consistent with the clown role he appears to play in school. James used more color dominant responses than the average boy his age, and correspondingly fewer in which color was subservient to form. This, together with his greater than average number of animal movement responses, suggested immaturity and a lack of emotional control.

On the Draw-A-Person Test, the figure appeared to be distorted, with emphasis on body size and a disproportionally small head. This possibly reflects feelings of inferiority in mental ability. The oversized shoulders on the figure may represent a need to appear strong and masculine. The body was square with the arms and legs hanging mechanically. This gave the figure the appearance of a robot. Such drawings sometimes represent a projection of being controlled by outside forces. They may signify a mechanical interest. James' hobbies and interests were not shown to be mechanical. The figure of the female, drawn later, was less than half the size of the male. It was drawn with arms behind the back. There were frequent erasures in the drawing of the female, compared to no erasures in the drawing of the male. Erasures are sometimes interpreted as indications of conflict regarding what the drawing represents. When asked who this drawing looked like, he said, "My mother, but it also looks like my teacher." The drawing of the male figure "could be myself".

On the Kahn Test of Symbol Arrangement, James symbolized the heart-shaped objects as "toys", and in the first and second arrangements, placed these objects on the end of the strip. However, on the fifth arrangement, he picked up the heart-shaped objects first, and put them in the first, second, and third segments of the strip. Later, in sorting, he placed the blue and transparent hearts in the LOVE category and the red heart in SMALL. The "P" object was called a "gun", and he liked this one most because it "offers protection". The white dog was described as "a poor puppy barking for food who is not liked by the other two dogs because he doesn't conform". On the recall section of the test, he guessed that he would remember the exact placement of two or three objects. He actually placed seven objects correctly. The large dog which he had called a "mother dog" was associated with SMALL in the sorting task, and the small black dog was placed with HATE. The cross was seen as a plus sign, symbolizing "arithmetic", and it was also associated with HATE.

James' ambivalence with the heart-shaped objects which he associated with LOVE, may reflect conflictual feelings regarding his mother. The test suggested the presence of a disruptive sibling rivalry, feelings of rejection, and a need for protection against a hostile environment. Loss of confidence in ability was indicated by his estimate of recall. Frustration expressed against a school associated object, the plus sign, was consistent with the use of school as an outlet for aggression. The test yielded a symbol pattern which was more typical of disturbed children than of normal 13-year olds. Comparison with the I.Q. indicates loss of effective symbolic functioning.

Conclusions and Summary

James was intellectually capable of doing his school work. Emotionally, he appeared to be less mature than other children of his age. This absence of emotional development may be related to feelings of rejection by the mother, with a carry-over of these feelings to his teacher. Testing supported the impression that James felt considerable hostility toward his younger brother, which could account for his combative attitude in the school.

Feelings of helplessness, affective deprivation, and a low estimate of self-worth, were projected. Testing suggested that James may have failed to show warm affection toward his parents because of a fear of being emotionally hurt. School offered James an outlet for his aggressions and the behavior problems in the classroom probably stem, in part, from a need for recognition. It is believed that the capacity to relate to people existed in this boy, in spite of the difficulties manifested in interpersonal relationships. It was suggested that a re-education of the parents, culminating in their accepting James as they do his younger brother, would speed emotional maturation and lessen the need for substitutes. James seemed to gain confidence by encouragement. In school, direction into athletic pursuits might do much to furnish outlets for the accumulated tensions and conflicts.

CASE II

Referral Information

The patient was a well dressed, unmarried woman of 35 years of age who was apprehended while stealing lingerie and bits of inexpensive jewelry from a department store. No previous history of criminal activity existed. This woman was employed as a secretary in a large business firm, and received a relatively high salary. She had several thousand dollars in a personal savings account. She declared that she did not know why she had stolen, but described the impulse as "irresistible". She said that she was afraid the impulse to steal would recur unless she obtained help.

The social worker's case study revealed that this patient had been raised by a critical father who discouraged all of her male admirers. Her mother had been weak and sickly as long as she could remember. There were no siblings. A younger sister had died in infancy. The family had always been poor, and the mother had worked as a seamstress when her health permitted. The patient had been sent to secretarial school by an uncle. Upon graduating, she found a job and sent money home regularly, as neither her father nor her mother were working. She lived frugally, saved money and avoided social contact with men because it made her feel guilty. Her contacts with the girls in the office were friendly, but formal. She always felt that she could not understand other people, and for this reason kept to herself. The patient had a birthday a month before the stealing incident. On her birthday she felt lonely, and spent the evening in her room crying. Two weeks later, a salesman working in the firm asked her for a date. She agreed, in spite of feelings of fear. During the evening she wanted to be friendly, but instead felt compelled to treat him coldly. Nevertheless, heavy petting ensued. Upon her return home, she felt depressed, guilty, and cried most of the night.

When interviewed by the psychiatrist, it was difficult to obtain longitudinal history, as she was a poor historian. It was difficult to get sufficient information to ascertain the degree of decompensation, or to arrive at a definite diagnostic conclusion with the information that was available. The psychiatrist requested psychological testing to assist in identifying the dynamics, and crystalizing his impressions that the patient had decompensated. It was also hoped that the severity and direction of this decompensation could be determined.

Interview Impression

The patient was a thin, small, but not unattractive woman, dressed in a blue suit, who wore little make-up. She entered the psychologist's office without reluctance. Although she stated that she feared testing, she co-operated throughout. Reaction time toward test stimuli ranged from average to slow.

Tests Administered

1. Thematic Apperception Test (Murray)
2. Rorschach Test of Personality Diagnosis.
3. Sentence Completion Test.
4. Draw-A-Person Test.
5. Kahn Test of Symbol Arrangement.
6. Minnesota Multiphasic Personality Inventory.

Test Findings

To Card 8 GF on the TAT, a girl in a meditative pose, the response was, "a lonely person who did not know how to find happiness". Her thoughts were described as "dreaming that someone would give her presents". In discussing the ending of the situation, the patient said, "no one will ever do anything for her—she will have to do everything for herself, just as I did".

Her response to Card 13 MF was "brother and sister". This is a rather unusual response for this scene. The man standing with his arm over his eyes, "is regretting that he does not permit anyone to visit his sister" (the girl lying partly nude on the bed). "She is not sick, but just unhappy over her brother's jealousy." The patient projected what appeared to be her own dynamics quite readily on this test. The brother and other restricting male authority figures seen, reflect the patient's attitude toward her father. The hopelessness and loneliness ascribed to the female figures mirrored the patient's own feelings.

On the Rorschach, there was only one response per card. Reaction time was relatively fast, except for Cards IV, VII, and X. Almost all of the responses were "wholes" such as "ballet dancer" on Card III, "sea lion" on Card IV, "clouds or bunnies" on Card VII. Color was a strong factor in concepts such as "under water scene" for Card X. Color, in general, outweighed human movement. The percentage of animal movement was higher than that expected in average records. The relatively high percentage of achromatic color responses (blackness of cards) support the TAT findings of depression and excessive reserve. This adjustment pattern is in direct conflict with the Rorschach signs of impulsiveness and affective lability. Maturity, as suggested by the human movement responses, was outweighed by the primitive instinctual drives as indicated by the animal movement and color reactions.

The Sentence Completion Test supports the presence of conflict in the way the patient views herself. *"When I was a child*, I was bad." *"My idea of a perfect woman* is being a good woman." *"I feel that my father* seldom loves anyone." Without hesitating the patient finished the phrase, *"My greatest mistake was* stealing"*. Denial and apparent lack of insight was suggested by, *"I could be perfectly happy if* this didn't happen".

On the Draw-A-Person Test, the patient drew what appeared to be a plain-looking, teen-aged child, but before completing it she drew lines across the picture, saying that she could not draw very well. She was induced to try again. Her second attempt represented a glamorous fashion model, very well drawn. When asked to draw a person of the opposite sex, she refused, saying that she knew she would not be able to draw a man.

On the Kahn Test of Symbol Arrangement, the patient obtained a Symbol Pattern which was consistent with hysterical neurosis. Depression was manifested by the placement of the anchor and the circle in DEAD, during the sorting task. The blue heart was the least liked object because: "I think a heart should be red. A blue heart makes me think of a sick heart." In sorting, the blue heart was the only one placed in LIVING. The stars, which were symbolized as "hope", were all associated with SMALL in the sorting task.

The hysterical impression of the KTSA Symbol Pattern was supported by the patient's scores on the Minnesota Multiphasic Personality Inventory. On the profile, hysteria score was highest, depression and hypochondriasis were also elevated. Other scores, including the psychopathic deviate scale, were not raised above what is expected in normal groups. The fact that neither the psychopathic deviate score nor the lie score were raised, was consistent with the absence of signs of character and behavior disorder in the rest of the battery.

Conclusion and Summary

Psychological testing indicated that the patient was caught in a situation in which inhibition and self-denial were in conflict with a strong need for self-indulgence. Projections were elicited suggesting that the patient suffered from having had a strict and jealous father, incapable of giving affection. Repression of self-expression, and lack of satisfying contacts with other persons, appeared to have stunted emotional maturity. The patient was depressed, but not suicidal. The patient was pessimistic about her future adjustment. The testing was not typical of character or behavior disorder, but rather suggested the presence of a hysterical neurosis. These individuals resort to the defense of repression in order to cope with their own impulses and the demands in the world about them. Perhaps the realization of oncoming age, combined with a series of precipitating events, caused sufficient weakening of customary adjustment mechanisms to liberate long dormant impulses for love and affection. In the absence of inability to relate to persons who could satisfy these needs, the patient tried to gratify them symbolically by the theft of "presents". No signs were elicited on any of the tests suggestive of defective reality awareness. There were no indications of incipient psychosis.

Case III

Referral Information

This 34-year old white male was seen 2 years before referral because of episodes of uneasiness and nervousness in his stomach, followed by light-headedness, and then visual disturbances. Neurological study, spinal fluid, EEG and skull x-rays were done in addition to the routine examinations. The EEG findings ranged from convulsive disorder to slight abnormality without definite pattern. He was placed on anticonvulsants with no improvement. The symptoms have become progressively worse. There had been two episodes of unconsciousness, but no incontinence or muscle activity. The neurological service referred this individual for psychological evaluation. "Patient has temporal lobe type seizures, becoming more frequent. His behavior suggests an organic syndrome with strong suspicion of neoplasm."

Interview Impression

The patient, a neatly dressed individual, appeared approximately 15 minutes early for his appointment. He was pleasant, friendly, and talked freely in a slow and deliberate manner. He apologized for the difficulty he had in pronunciation of words, which he attributed to previous stuttering in early life. During the interview it was noted that he continuously tapped his foot on the floor or adjusted his glasses. The patient described the onset of his symptoms and marital difficulty one year previously. He stated that his "beautiful ex-ballet dancer" wife had fallen in love with a younger man, his best friend. They separated for approximately 6 months. The wife returned and since then the patient has had a "very happy relationship" with her. The patient blamed himself for some of his marital difficulty, stating he spent too much time playing golf. He expressed concern over his increasing loss in sexual interest. He felt he was becoming more irritable and had some difficulty with his memory. He finished high school, described himself as a good student, and was always interested in mechanical things.

Tests Administered

1. The Wechsler Adult Intelligence Scale.
2. The Bender Motor Visual Gestalt Test.
3. The Weigl–Goldstein–Scheerer Cube and Color Form Tests.
4. The Kahn Test of Symbol Arrangement.
5. Rorschach Test of Personality Diagnosis.
6. The Draw-A-Person Test.
7. Tests for Aphasia and Handedness.

Test Findings

On the Wechsler the patient obtained a full scale I.Q. of 108, a verbal I.Q. of 119, and a performance I.Q. of 92. A comparison of HOLD with DON'T HOLD sub-tests yields an 0·9 percent estimated loss after correction for age. This is not considered significant. The psychograph drawn from the subscores roughly follows Wechsler's criteria for organic brain disease, with the exception that the patient obtained a higher block design score, and a lower vocabulary score than is typical. Low vocabulary scores occur in brain damaged patients with limited educational background. This patient had a high school education. The lowest subscore was digit symbol, suggesting loss in the capacity for new learning requiring visual-motor speed. Such loss is encountered among depressed patients as well as among those with various types of organic impairment.

The Bender reproductions were, in the main, within normal limits. No significant distortions of motor gestalten were elicited. The performance suggests an absence of diffuse cortical atrophy and of pathology affecting the visual-motor-spacial orientation. These findings were corroborated by the results of the Weigl–Goldstein–Scheerer tests. The patient had no difficulty with the cube designs. He was also able to shift spontaneously from the form to the color principle of grouping the pieces. Patients with gross, diffuse deterioration, or those with focal lesions in cortical areas affecting visual-motor co-ordination, would be expected to have difficulty with these tests. The absence of such difficulty is consistent with the high block design subscore on the Wechsler.

The Symbol Pattern on the Kahn Test of Symbol Arrangement approximates that expected in an obsessive-compulsive neurosis. A number of signs typically seen in non-psychotic patients with organic brain disease were also present and overlapped with the compulsive pattern. Among the overlapping signs were: extreme rigidity in arrangements, lowered capacity for symbolic abstraction, meticulous naming, or placement of objects. The fact that there were no errors in the recall task is more typical of compulsives. The very slow reaction time is more characteristic of organics than compulsives. The good recall performance suggests that the patient was not malingering. The association of the phallic object and the female symbol with SMALL in the sorting task may represent projection of inferiority in psychosexual activities, mentioned by the patient in the interview.

The Rorschach elicited four out of the ten Piotrowski signs of organic brain disease. These were: prolonged response time, no human movement concepts, less than fifteen responses, and indications of impotence. A mild tendency to perseverate was also present. Form responses were better than expected among patients with organic psychological deficit. Frequent reference to card symmetry supports the KTSA findings of a compulsive element in the personality. The patient utilized a number of concepts frequently employed by those who have suffered emotional trauma. One contamination occurred. Obsessive-compulsives are the only clinical group, other than psychotics, among whom contaminated responses are likely to occur. With the exception of one response, color was loosely and ineffectively utilized. Color naming—a prominent sign of brain pathology—was not elicited. In general, the Rorschach corresponds to what some researchers have indicated as a typical pattern of epileptic or convulsive states. On the Draw-A-Person Test, the patient drew crude figures that appeared to be the work of an immature person. Both male and female figures were bizarre in certain respects. The limbs of the figures appeared to be strung together, with a joint emphasis suggestive of projected feelings of body disorganization. Inappropriate shading, midline emphasis, slight disproportioning, poor synthesis, together with the mildly bizarre qualities, suggest the presence of a defective self-image, often associated with the presence of organic disease.

Conclusions and Summary

Psychological testing suggest the presence of an obsessive-compulsive orientation. Test signs of this condition—such as lack of flexibility, cautiousness, hesitation, prolonged reaction time overlap with signs characteristic of patients with organic psychological deficit. In some respects the findings were contradictory: we would not expect organics to have such good recall and psychomotor ability; nor compulsives to have such prolonged reaction times, perplexity, and defective concept formation. No aphasic signs were elicited. The slight speech difficulty noted is believed to be a residual of severe stammering in childhood. Some evidence of conflict of lateral dominance was found. One of the tests approximated the expected patterns of convulsive states. If there is a lesion present, it has not vitally affected the cortical areas of visual-motor co-ordination. Gross or diffuse cortical damage is unlikely. There is no significant intellectual loss. Organic signs were weak and scattered. The total test pattern is not completely typical of organic brain disease. On the other hand, the test results cannot be satisfactorily explained on a functional basis alone. Some organic signs were consistently found in a number of the tests. To this extent, the psychological examination gives qualified support to the neurological impression of possible organic brain disease.

No psychological report is as good as a face-to-face discussion between the psychologist and the person who referred the patient. Too often we are inclined to substitute written reports for personal meetings. Psychological reports are only abstracts of the information that is available. Time limitations and the pressure of work requires the psychologist to limit his written evaluation to cover the points which he thinks are of interest to the referrant as indicated by the reasons for referral. Often there is additional material of value which may be gleaned from the psychological test performance that comes to light only when the case is discussed in conference. Finally, whether our evaluation pertains to identification of disease, vocational goals, or to educational placement, we must always keep in mind that pride in the ingenuity of our methods, should be matched by humbleness in the face of the unsurmountable limitations of our science.

BIBLIOGRAPHY

1. AMES, Louise, LEARNED, Janet, METRAUX, Ruth, and WALKER, R., *Child Rorschach Responses: Developmental Trends from Two to Ten Years*, Paul B. Hoeber, Inc., New York, 1952.
2. AMMONS, R. B., and AMMONS, Helen, *The Full Range Picture Vocabulary Test*, Psychological Test Specialists, Missoula, 1948.
3. AMMONS, R. B., BUTLER, Margaret, and HERZIG, S. A., *The Vocational Apperception Test*, Southern Universities Press, Louisville, 1949.
4. ARTHUR, Grace, *Arthur Point Scale of Performance Tests*, Form I, C. H. Stoelting Co., Chicago, 1943.
5. ARTHUR, Grace, *Arthur Point Scale of Performance Tests*, Form II, Psychological Corp., New York, 1947.
6. BECK, S. J., "The Rorschach Test as applied to a feeble-minded group", *Arch. Psychol.*, **136**, 84 (1932).
7. BELL, J. E., *Projective Techniques: A Dynamic Approach to the Study of Personality*, Longmans, Green & Co., Inc., New York, 1948.
8. BELLAK, L., and BELLAK, Sonya, *Children's Apperception Test*, rev. ed., C.P.S. Co., New York, 1949–50.
9. BENDER, Lauretta, *The Visual-Motor Gestalt Test and Its Clinical Use*, American Orthopsychiatric Association, Inc., New York, 1938.
10. BENDER, Lauretta, *Instructions for the Use of Visual-Motor Gestalt Test*, American Orthopsychiatric Association, Inc., New York, 1946.
11. BENTON, A. L., *The Revised Visual Retention Test. Clinical and Experimental Applications*, The State University of Iowa, Iowa City, 1955.
12. BLUM, G. S., *The Blacky Pictures: A Technique for the Exploration of Personality Dynamics*, Psychological Corp., New York, 1950.
13. BUCK, J. N., "The H.T.P Technique", Monogr. Suppl. No. 5, *J. clin. Psychol.*, 1948.
14. BUHLER, Charlotte, and KELLY, Gayle, *The World Test: A Measurement of Emotional Disturbance*, Psychological Corp., New York, 1941.
15. BURGEMEISTER, Bessie, BLUM, L. H., and LORGE, I., *Columbia Mental Maturity Scale*, rev. ed., Psychological Corp., New York, 1959.
16. CATTELL, P., *The Measurement of Intelligence of Infants and Young Children*, Psychological Corp., New York, 1940.
17. CHARLES, D. C., "Ability and accomplishment of persons earlier judged mentally deficient", *Genet. Psychol. Monogr.*, **47**, 3–71 (1953).

18. DELP, H. A. (Rev.), "The Wechsler Intelligence Scale for Children", The Fourth Mental Measurements Yearbook, 1953, p. 363.

19. DOERKEN, H., and KRAL, A. V., "The psychological differentiation of organic brain lesions and their localization by means of the Rorschach Test", Paper read at the 107th Annual Meeting of the American Psychiatric Association, Cincinnati, 1951, and *Amer. J. Psychiat.*, **108** (1952).

20. EISENSON, J., *Examining for Aphasia and Related Disturbances*, rev. ed., Psychological Corp., New York, 1954.

21. GOLDSTEIN, K., and SCHEERER, M., "Abstract and concrete behavior, and experimental study with special tests", *Psychol. Monogr.*, **43**, 1–151 (1941).

22. GOODENOUGH, Florence, *Goodenough Intelligence Test: Draw-A-Man.* World Book Co., Yonkers, 1926.

23. GOODENOUGH, Florence, *Mental Testing: Its History, Principles, and Applications*, Rinehart & Co., Inc., New York, 1949.

24. GRASSI, J. R., *The Grassi Block Substitution Test for Measuring Brain Pathology*, Charles C. Thomas, Springfield, 1953.

25. GUIRDHAM, A., "The Rorschach Test in epileptics", *J. Ment. Sci.*, 1935.

26. HARRIS, A. J., *Harris Tests of Lateral Dominance*, Psychological Corp., New York, 1947.

27. HARROWER-ERICKSON, M. R., "Personality changes accompanying cerebral lesions: Rorschach studies of patients with cerebral tumors", *Arch. Neurol. Psychiat.*, **43**, 1081–1107 (1940).

28. HARTWELL, S., WALTON, R. E., ANDREW, G., and HUTT, M., *The Michigan Picture Test*, Science Research Associates, Chicago, 1955.

29. HATHAWAY, S. R., and McKINLEY, J. C., *Minnesota Multiphasic Personality Inventory*, rev. ed., Psychological Corp., New York, 1951.

30. HUNT, W. A., *The Clinical Psychologist*, Charles C. Thomas, Springfield, 1956.

31. HUNT, H. F., *The Hunt-Minnesota Test for Organic Brain Damage*, University of Minnesota Press, Minneapolis, 1943.

32. KAHN, T. C., "Cross validation of the organic brain pathology scale for Test of Symbol Arrangement", *J. consult. Psychol.*, **19**, 2 (1955).

33. KAHN, T. C., *The Kahn Test of Symbol Arrangement. Clinical Manual*, Perceptual and Motor Skills, Monograph Supplement No. 1, Psychological Test Specialists, Missoula, Montana, 1957.

34. KAHN, T. C., and FINK, H. H., "Comparison of normal with emotionally disturbed children by the Kahn Test of Symbol Arrangement", Paper read at the American Psychological Association, New York, 1957.

35. KLOPFER, B., "Rorschach signs of nonpsychotic organics-idiopathic epileptics. Adapted from Lectures by Bruno Klopfer, University of California, 1949.

36. KLOPFER, B., and KELLEY, D. M., *The Rorschach Technique*, World Book Company, New York, 1946.
37. LEITER, R. G., *Leiter International Performance Scale*, rev. manual, Psychological Service Center Press, Washington, D.C., 1948.
38. LOWENFELD, Margaret, *The Lowenfeld Mosaic Test*, Newman, Neame, Ltd., London, 1954.
39. LOWENFELD, Margaret, "The nature and use of the Lowenfeld World Technique in work with children and adults", *J. Psychol.*, **30**, 325–331.
40. McFATE, Margurite, and ORR, Frances, "Through adolescence with the Rorschach", Reprinted from *Rorschach Res. Exch.*, and *J. proj. Tech.*, **13**, No. 3 (1949).
41. MACHOVER, Karen, *Personality Projection in the Drawing of the Human Figure*, Charles C. Thomas, Springfield, 1949.
42. MILES, W. R., *A-B-C Vision Test for Ocular Dominance*, Psychological Corp., New York, 1946.
43. MORENO, J. L., *Psychodrama*, Beacon House, New York, 1946.
44. MURRAY, H. A., *et al.*, *Thematic Apperception Test Manual*, Harvard University Press, Cambridge, 1943.
45. MURRAY, H. A., *et al.*, *Explorations in Personality*, Oxford University Press, New York, 1938.
46. MURPHY, P. D., BOLINGER, R. W., and FERRIMAN, M. R., "Screening neuropsychiatric patients by means of the Kahn Test of Symbol Arrangement", *Behavioral Sci.*, **3**, No. 4, 344–346 (1958).
47. MURPHY, P. D., FERRIMAN, M. R., and BOLINGER, R. W., "The Kahn Test of Symbol Arrangement as an aid to psychodiagnosis", *J. consult. Psychol.*, **21**, No. 6, 503–505 (1957).
48. PEACHER, W. G. (Rev.), "Harris Tests of Lateral Dominance", The Fourth Mental Measurements Yearbook, The Gryphon Press, Highland Park, 1953.
49. PHILLIPS, L., and SMITH, J. G., *Rorschach Interpretation: Advanced Technique*, Grune and Stratton, New York, 1953.
50. PIOTROWSKI, Z., "On the Rorschach Method and its application in organic disturbances of the central nervous system", *Rorschach Res. Exch.*, **1**, 23–40 (1936–37), and *Kwart. Psychol.*, **9**, 29–41 (1937).
51. RAPAPORT, D., GILL, M., and SCHAFER, R., *Diagnostic Psychological Testing*, Vol. I, The Yearbook Publishers, Inc., Chicago, 1946.
52. RAPAPORT, D., GILL, M., and SCHAFER, R., *Diagnostic Psychological Testing*, Vol. II, The Yearbook Publishers, Inc., Chicago, 1947.
53. RORSCHACH, H., *Psychodiagnostics, A Diagnostic Test Based on Perception*, Grune and Stratton, Inc., New York, 1942.
54. RUCH, F. L., *Psychology and Life*, Scott, Foresman & Co., Chicago, 1958.
55. SCHAFER, R., *The Clinical Application of Psychological Tests*, International Universities Press, Inc., New York, 1948.

56. SHIPLEY, W. C., "A self-administering scale for measuring intellectual impairment and deterioration", *J. Psychol.*, **9**, 371–377 (1940).
57. SHNEIDMAN, E. S., *The Make-A-Picture Story Test*, Psychological Corp., New York, 1949.
58. SHNEIDMAN, E. S., *Manual for the Make-A-Picture Story Test*, Projective Techniques Monograph, No. 2, The Society for Projective Techniques and Rorschach Institute, New York, 1952.
59. SYMONDS, P. M., *Adolescent Fantasy: An Investigation of the Picture-Story Method of Personality Study*, Columbia University Press, New York, 1949.
60. TERMAN, L. M., and MERRILL, M. A., *Measuring Intelligence*, Houghton Mifflin Co., Boston, 1937.
61. TINKER, M. A. (Rev.), "A-B-C Vision Test for Ocular Dominance", *The Fourth Mental Measurements Yearbook*, The Gryphon Press, Highland Park, 1953.
62. TM 8-242, AFM 160-45, "Military Clinical Psychology". Department of the Army Technical Manual, Department of the Air Force Manual, United States Government Printing Office, Washington, 1951.
63. WECHSLER, D., *The Measurement of Adult Intelligence*, 3rd ed., The Williams & Wilkins Co., Baltimore, 1944.
64. WECHSLER, D., *Wechsler Intelligence Scale for Children*, Psychological Corp., New York, 1949.
65. WECHSLER, D., *The Measurement and Appraisal of Adult Intelligence*, The Williams & Wilkins Co., Baltimore, 1958.
66. WELLS, F. L., and RUESCH, J., *Mental Examiner's Handbook*, rev. ed., Psychological Corp., New York, 1945.
67. WERTHEIMER, M., "Studies in the theory of gestalt psychology", *Psychol. Forsch.*, **4**, 300 (1923).
68. YATES, A. J., "The validity of some psychological tests of brain damage", *Psychol. Bull.*, **51**, 359–379 (1954).

L

INDEX